Timeless

Joan Hallam

Acknowledgements

Thank you to all those who have supported my writing. With special thanks to Stephen Evans and Veronica Hyde who hosted Writing Well and Speaking Well without whom this book would never have been written. Thank you to all my writing group for your encouragement and especially to Delsierene Waul, Phil Page and Stephen Evans for your immense help with editing and publishing. Special thanks and love go to my husband Bill Hallam for his patience and help whilst I completed this book.

Dedicated with all my love to Ellen Elizabeth Brockway and Michael Henry Curran.

To their children, grandchildren, great-grandchildren, great-great-grandchildren

And those who are still to come.

With a glow of pride and a deep sense of loss, you were never mine alone. I watched you grow. I fed you tales and nurtured your wholeness. I dwelt on every word. Not on my own did I grow you to who you are. I searched for what gave you warmth and made you whole. You fed me back your love, your warmth, your sorrows and strength.

Timeless is love. Timeless is family. Telling the stories makes memories timeless.

Now you will live forever timelessly.

Daniel Curran *m* **Ellen Elizabeth Keily   (m Jan 1875)**

1851 - 1889?   1854 – 1942

|

|John Joseph 1876-1955

|Patrick Stephen 1877-1906

| Michael Henry Curran (Harry) 1880-1916

|Bridget Delia Curran 1881-1961

|Mary Curran 1884-1944

| Kathleen Curran1886-1911

| Helena Curran 1888-1960

Michael Henry Curran (Harry) *m*

Eileen *m* Sidney	Kathleen *m* Wilfred	George *m* Norah
1908-1990	*1908-1985*	*1910-1979*
Patricia	Frederick	Maureen
Anthony	Joan	Eileen
Geoffrey		Michael
		Peter

4

James Albert Brockway *m* **Elizabeth Mary Smith**
(m Oct 1871)
1847 – 1908   1846 – 1922

|

| Henry George Brockway 1877-

| Edward Brockway 1879-1882

| Ellen Elizabeth Brockway 1881-1952

| Ann Belle Brockway 1885-

| James Albert Brockway 1890-

Ellen Elizabeth Curran (m May 1907)

| |

Nora *m* Herbert   Francis *m* Kathleen

1912-1993   *1914-2008*

| |

Joan Elizabeth   Christine

Barbara   Pauline

Dennis

Andrea

Madeleine

Introduction One

James trudged along the shaded leafy lane. Everything he owned he carried with him and there were still several miles to go. He would call and see his Grandfather at Donhead St Mary's on the way but he wasn't going to stay, no matter what his family said. He knew his Grandfather would like him to stay and learn to be a stonemason like himself but he was old now and couldn't teach him. Adventure called James now.

St Mary's hadn't been his home since he was eight years old. His father had died when he was just four years old and his brother Henry had been a baby. His mother had struggled and found it very difficult to manage. With much sorrow, and to keep them from the workhouse, she had been obliged to let him go into an apprenticeship with a farmer several miles away. There were other apprentice plough boys there, one of them had come from the same village. He had been working and living with the hired hands for eight years, in the outbuildings of the farm, getting what learning he could. It had been a hard upbringing, the farmer strict, and boys soon became men. James had learned to look after the tall Shire horses that pulled the ploughs but he was itching now so see something of life.

From St Mary's, after saying his farewells to family, he walked along the lanes until he came to the main route to London. He would catch a mail coach and pay for his journey from what little he had of his pay from the farm. But he wasn't going to London. He was heading for Portsmouth intending to see the world. He was going to join Queen Victoria's Royal Navy. He could almost smell the sea, but that was his imagination. For several hundred years neither he nor anyone in his family had ever been further than Blandford or Salisbury.

Introduction Two

The crossing was tough and the sea troubled as they huddled together on the deck. Pulling her cloak around her, Ellen opened one of her bags and shared some food between them. Bread and cheese, she had haggled for on the market before leaving Dublin. From Clonmel, they had made their way to Dublin to catch the Liverpool ferry. Ellen with her seven children aged three to fourteen, the eldest three being boys, gathered around several large bags, packed tightly with all their worldly goods. She was in a desperate state; her husband Daniel had sailed to America to start a new life for the family only to die a few months after arriving.

Using the last of the wages that Daniel had sent from America, and now homeless, Ellen was on her way to Manchester at the invitation of her sister Catherine, seven years younger but married and childless as yet. She had written, promising to find work and schooling for them in this bustling city. Ellen was proud and although she had shed many private tears for Daniel, she always appeared calm and organised with the children. They were spotlessly clean and well-mannered as she expected them to be. There would be no begging on their part. She had seen too much of that in the devastating times in Clonmel; travelling beggars desperate for food for their families. Not her, she would work every hour she could when she got to Manchester. From the fresh green fields of their smallholding in Waterford, she had no idea of the dark and smoky town she was taking them to. The two eldest boys would be able to find some work. She would work herself and her sister would help her with the little ones. A whole new beginning. What was there not to look forward to. With a prayer to St Patrick and one to St Christopher the patron saint of travellers, they were on their way.

Chapter One

January 1881 saw massive snowfalls in Southern England. For two weeks it snowed and we were living in a white wonderland. The covering had been so heavy that a roof in old Portsmouth had caved in under the weight. An eerie stillness filled the air. The soft blanketing muffled the sound of the horses and carts on the cobbles. Transport came to a standstill as snowdrifts reached halfway up the lamp posts. Heavy ice clung to the masts of the ships in the docks weighing them down. Red, raw hands traded baskets of fish from the boats as they returned to port.

Three weeks later the remains of the drifts still hung around in icy pockets against the walls and the abandoned snowman in our backyard had been reduced to a mound of ice with two coal-black eyes askew. The temperatures had been so low that our supply of coal was drastically reduced as Mama tried to keep the house warm. Now the fire in the bedroom was being built up by Mama's sister and the snow-wet coals sizzled and spat as they hit the heat. Mama sat up in bed holding a small warm bundle in her arms. One little red-faced baby girl had whooshed into the world on Sunday 20th February 1881.

"A child that is born on the Sabbath Day is bonny and blithe and good and gay." I had a lot to live up to. I was born Ellen Elizabeth Brockway at 12 Abingdon Road, Portsmouth but my family always called me Nellie. At the time I had two older brothers, Henry who was six and Edward aged two. My Pa, James Albert Brockway, stood just five feet nine inches tall with light brown hair and grey eyes. His fair skin meant he sometimes suffered from the sun and sea breezes. Arriving from the Wiltshire countryside at sixteen he had joined the navy earning £9 a year and served for ten years as a stoker then from the age of twenty-six as a cook 2nd class earning £30 a year on various ships of the Royal Navy.

Mama stayed at home and looked after our family as all married women did. Our house was in a row of weathered terraced houses in the old part of Portsmouth near the docks. We shared the house with the Stroud family. Henry Stroud was a brass moulder and he and his wife Jane had just one son who was a baby a year older than me. We rented the house and let rooms out, which was quite common in those days to help make ends meet. I am not sure if my father was there when I was born as he was serving on the HMS Malabar at the time but by April that year, he was moored in Portsmouth Harbour. Who knows if he had been there when my brothers were born, perhaps he was away at sea then. Mama would have understood and been accustomed to this sort of life as her father was a ship's engineer who also travelled the world with the Royal Navy. She was born Elizabeth Mary Smith, in 1849 in a small Dartmoor village called Peter Tavy, near Tavistock, Devon. The birthplace of her mother. As the eldest of five children and with the family they moved to various naval bases until settling in Portsmouth where she met and married Pa on October 8th 1871 at St Mary's Church, Fratton Road, Portsea.

Before I was one, my brother Edward passed away in January. Our family must have been distraught. Of course, I don't remember the events around the time as I was too young but I do remember my sister being born on 13th June 1885 when I was four. She was born at home as all babies were and Mama once again had help from one of her sisters, my aunt, who came to stay with us, and a local midwife. We were all sent out to play in the street whilst we waited and waited until at last Auntie came out and said we could come in and see our new baby. Mama was sitting up in bed holding a bundle of blankets. A tiny pink wrinkled face was just visible and as I gazed in wonder, her unfocused eyes blinked open and shut again. Mama smiled at us and told us how lucky we were to have such a beautiful new sister and she was to be called Ann Belle. Now, although I thought I would love her, here was another little girl to take all the attention I had received from my parents and elder brother.

A year later I eagerly joined my friends at our local church school. I loved my lessons and would regale my family with all the new things I had learned to show them how clever I was. My friends all lived nearby and we played out on the cobbled streets around us. Ours was the freedom of innocence. Nothing to fear as we ran around the local streets. Neighbours were neighbours then, and there were always adults around who knew who you were and kept an eye on what was going on. There was always the smell of the sea and the clamour and clatter from the docks nearby. The clanging of the masts, the shouts from the dockworkers, metalled cartwheels and horses' hooves clopping on the cobbles as they hurried their loads to and from the docks filled the air with a cacophony of noise. The deep-throated blasts of the ships' sirens breaking into it all as they navigated their way through the Solent to the docks, and the unending screeches of the seagulls bombarding the fishing boats as they came in. So long as we were around when we were shouted in for tea time or bedtime we were free. A quick hand and face wash sufficed in the week. Saturday was the day for bathing and hair wash, taking turns in the tin bath in front of the fire. Hair brushed and brushed until it was dried by the heat of the fire. All clean and respectable for church on Sunday morning.

Most of my friends had fathers who were in the Royal Navy or worked in the dockyard so we were used to their being away most of the time. Mothers were the matriarchs and ran the households so had to be strong women who could cope without a husband around. It was their responsibility to raise the children and discipline them. This made for some very interesting characters in our neighbourhood. It's amazing how this builds your character without realising it.

Pa was serving on the HMS Malabar, a troop carrier, which travelled to India and we didn't see him for months at a time. It seemed like years to a child of my age. How we loved the shout, in his West Country accent, from the front door.

"Where are you my darlings? Your Pa is home".

We ran to be first to throw ourselves into his arms as he dropped his kitbag from his shoulder. Mama must have heard his ship had docked, as she had gotten herself all dressed up and taken off her pinafore, and a delicious smell was coming from the kitchen. In his big comfy chair by the fire, we would snuggle and squash onto his lap of an evening as he filled our imagination with stories of the places he had been and how colourful they were, the amazing animals he had seen, elephants and monkeys walking down the streets. There were large white pelicans with pouches under their bills and egrets with long legs for wading in the waters. How amazing. And the heat, he told us, was sometimes so unbearable they could hardly breathe or the monsoon rain which was like standing under a big tap.

It was magical for us when Pa returned from months at sea but some of our friends lived in fear of their drunken fathers coming home from one of the inns on the Hard, causing mayhem in the home which had been happy during their absence.

We had an outside toilet in the backyard. The rooms in the house were dark, always shaded by net panels and heavy curtains with the only lighting being gaslight. I was only small so the furniture although sparse, looked large and dark to me. Scattered with rugs, the floor was covered in an oilcloth which was washed and polished every week. Around the house were foreign treasures Pa had brought back from his travels abroad. Carved elephants from India stood on the tall mantelpiece, silk cushions and mosaic vases that Mama loved. Woe betides anyone of us who tried to touch her precious gifts.

Around 1886 after serving two ten year contracts in the Navy, first as a stoker and then as a ship's cook second class, my Pa left the Navy and moved us all along the coast to a village called Emsworth on the outskirts of Portsmouth. This was a place busy with the manufacturing of everything related to ships and boats; sailcloth, sacking, rope, twine, and fishing nets. There was also a coastal trade in oyster fishing for which the village had long been celebrated.

It was a beautiful village with grasslands and tidal marshes around it. The marshes were a plentiful source of food for migrating birds that landed there in seasonal flocks. There was still the smell of the sea and the clamour of the harbour, but gone were my friends who knew me. Playing out in the street, I hovered around our front door hoping that one of the girls would come and talk to me. Slowly I got to know the children on our street. Now I had to start friendships all over again but how lovely it was to have Pa at home all the time.

Pa set himself up in business as "Brockway Hauliers" from No1 Sultan Road. The end house on a terraced row. We had two rooms downstairs and two rooms upstairs with an outside toilet but there was a large yard next to it where Pa was able to keep his horse and cart. He was in much demand and was in a prime spot across the road from the railway station, and next to a public house. He was used to keeping horses. As a young boy of around eight years old in Donhead St Mary's, Wiltshire he had been apprenticed to a farmer, several miles away, as a ploughboy. He lived and worked on the farm, run by a very harsh taskmaster, with several farmhands and apprentice boys like himself. When he reached the age of sixteen, he left for Portsmouth to join the Royal Navy. My eldest brother Henry joined the business as soon as he left school at fourteen and was apprenticed to Pa as a "carrier's apprentice". I sometimes wonder did he want to or was it expected of him. He certainly would have been a great help in the business as it grew. As children we didn't have much choice in the work we were to do after leaving school. It was decided by our parents, who secured the jobs for us.

I had started school at five years old in Portsea but now had to start going to a new school in Emsworth. That was quite daunting, to have to walk into a classroom where everyone knew each other and had their own best friends. I knew no one and didn't know the school routine. I kept to myself for a while and watched the others until I was eventually able to quietly slip into a group of girls naturally. I always felt a little bit on the outside but managed. My sister Ann Belle, who was born just before we moved to Emsworth, started her schooling there so she didn't have the same problems. She already knew most people in her class, from playing out, and she had lots of friends. Just before she started school, we had another addition to the family.

My youngest brother James Albert (named after Pa) was born on August 10th 1890. There was lots of excitement at having another son and brother. I was nine and as you can imagine nine-year-old girls love babies. I pushed him around the streets in his baby carriage drawing oohs and aahs from the local ladies. It's amazing how we ever managed in a two-up, two-down house, outside toilet and no bathroom, two adults with a new baby, Henry a teenage boy, myself and sister Ann Belle. This was normal at the time and much larger

14

families lived in similar accommodation. But we had Pa at home and ours was a loving home.

While Mama was getting used to having another baby I was expected to help with a lot of chores around the house and felt quite important to be doing work that Mama usually did. I tried to get my sister Ann Belle to help but she was only five and just wanted to go out and play with her friends. I did get to play out when I had helped. We played with hoops and sticks, bowling them along the cobbled streets, which made them jump around quite erratically. It was a sight to see, long-haired girls in dark dresses with white pinafores over them, black stockings and laced boots. Boys in shirts and waistcoats, knee-length breeches, always a cap, long socks, and buckled shoes. Some of the poorer children ran barefoot but Mama always made sure we had shoes or boots to wear.

We learned our lessons at school from what the teacher had written on the blackboard. We had to learn by heart and repeat this information together in front of the teacher. Even though we wrote on slates our handwriting was immaculate. It had to be or else there might be a knuckle rapping. We learned to read, write and mathematics. Not to a high standard, but most of us were quite capable. We all paid attention because if you didn't there was sometimes a long bamboo cane standing threateningly in the corner next to the teacher's desk. Looking back, we were so lucky to have the education we did when lots of children in those days didn't. Often it was because they needed to go out to work and help to support their families. If they lived on a farm, schooling came second when all hands were needed for lambing or harvesting. Skills like sewing, mending, embroidery, and knitting were mostly taught to us by our mothers. We were never allowed to sit with idle hands. "Idle hands are the devil's workshop" as our teacher was always telling us.

Our schooling might have been basic but I left with quite a rounded knowledge including a passion for reading anything I could lay my hands on including the family bible.

Chapter Two

It was usual in those days to leave school around fourteen and go to work as Henry had. For girls, the most opportunities for work were in service as it was a real status symbol to have a housemaid. Pa still had his connections with naval personnel and did well to arrange a position for me as a housemaid to Mrs Holbrook, a "widow of means", and her son Charles who was a master mariner. How exciting it would be as they lived in the newer Southsea area of Portsmouth. Even so, I was rather nervous about leaving home and family. I would only have a Sunday afternoon off with just enough time to travel home to see Mama and Pa. Maybe I would have some time off in the evening if Mrs Holbrook allowed when my work was done.

Mama had shown me how to do lots of household chores and given me handy tips but told me that I should listen to Mrs Holbrook who would have her own ideas of how she wanted me to do things. As my starting day drew near, I became a bit weepy in the quiet of my bedroom. I didn't want to let Mama and Pa think I was ungrateful for them having arranged a good position for me, I was going to miss them all. Some of my girlfriends from Emsworth had already gone into service in Portsmouth and I consoled myself with the thoughts that I might bump into them as I ran my errands.

The day arrived and I rose with apprehension. It was a lovely Spring morning and the sun warmed the day. At least it wasn't raining for my journey on Pa's cart. The last night in my own bed had already gone, now my last breakfast with the family. Henry teased me that he would be having my share of the food from now on but Mama scolded him and told him to behave. I was thinking that they would all be carrying on their lives just like this but without me. I'm sure Mama was holding back a tear or two. I caught her a few times dabbing her cheeks with a hankie. Ann Belle said she would help Mama a bit more now that I was leaving. She was the big girl in the house now. Pa came in and said the horse and cart were ready and took my valise for me.

Dressed in my outdoor coat and hat I hugged Mama and Ann Belle, reached up to Henry and with a kiss and hug for little James I climbed up onto Pa's cart with my bag. I had packed one spare set of undergarments; long drawers, stockings, bodice and corset, my toiletries and soft shoes for indoors. Mama had given me a small bible. It had been given to her and she now wished me to have it. She said that I should read it every night and from it, take any consolation I might need. I smiled weakly at Pa and he assured me that Mrs Holbrook would be a very fair mistress to me.

We reached Southsea travelling in along Lawrence Road, crossing Albert Road and onto Saxe Weimar Road. This was not Portsmouth as I remembered it. This area was almost all newly built. The roads were wider and the houses bigger than where we used to live. We turned into Allens Road and I was pleasantly surprised to see such lovely big bay-windowed houses. They had small front gardens with low walls and at intervals along the pavement were young cherry trees just coming into bud. This was a very grand area. We arrived at number six and Pa pulled the horse and cart up for us to get off. He helped me down and picking up my bag, led me to the front door. I stood trembling with nerves as the bell rang.

The door was opened by a housemaid who invited us in to meet Mrs Holbrook. A grand lady she looked, dressed fashionably in a long, tight waisted gown, as she entered the parlour. Her hair was pinned up in the latest style and she had the kindest smile for me. She told me to take my bag up to the attic room at the top of the house which would be my room, while she spoke to Pa.

The maid took me up two flights of stairs and opened the door into a small room with a sloped ceiling. There was a window looking out over the back yard and the houses behind. In the distance and between the roofs I could just see the sea. It had a bare wooden floor with just one rag rug. Along one wall there was a single iron bedstead with a pillow and clean white sheets covered with a grey woollen blanket. Against another wall stood a chest of three drawers with a mirror and a washbowl and jug. Three large drawers for the small number of belongings I had brought with me seemed more than ample. Behind the door, there was a hook on which hung my new uniform. This was to be my home for the foreseeable future. It was very impersonal at the time but I thought I might be able to change that. And anyway, I now had a whole room to myself! I said my goodbyes to Pa with a lingering hug and kisses and promised to write to them all at home. I smiled and whispered to him that I liked Mrs Holbrook and the house and thought I would be very happy here.

Over the next week, I was instructed in all my household duties by the maid. She was called Annie and would be leaving as soon as I was fully instructed. She had been with Mrs Holbrook and her son for some time now and had enjoyed her work but was leaving to get married and at present would just call in daily as I had taken over her room.

On a Monday, which was always washday no matter the weather, I would rise at five o'clock and fill the copper boiler in the basement with around six buckets of water, from the brass tap over the sink, and light the gas underneath it. There was no running hot water. The washing was separated into whites and coloureds. When the water was hot enough, I baled some out into a wooden tub and put the coloureds in to soak. The whites were put into the copper and set to boil with carbolic soap and soda.

Fire grates were cleaned out and new fires set. Rooms swept and fires lit in the downstairs rooms if needed. Breakfast was prepared and laid out for Mrs Holbrook, and her son when he was home. After breakfast had been served the pots were cleared and washed, once again boiling water on the kitchen range.

Back in the basement, some of the coloureds were agitated in the wooden tub with a wooden dolly, a stick with three small legs on the end, to move them around in the soapy water. After washing, everything was put through a mangle, two rubber rollers which, when turned with a handle, squeezed the water out of them. I had to rinse in clean water and mangle several times to get the soap out and each time clean water had to be fetched. With the whites, the last rinse was in blue water from a "Dolly Blue" bag, which was a muslin cloth tied around a small cube of blue substance and kept in a bowl of water. This gave the whites a brighter look.

Starch was used on tablecloths, collars, and handkerchiefs to give them a good finish. I made the starch from granules mixed first with cold water then boiling water. If the water wasn't hot enough the starch would not thicken and if not stirred quickly enough it would go lumpy. I didn't always get that right the first time.

When the weather was fine, I pegged the washing out on the washing lines strung from one end of the yard and back again and propped high with a wooden prop. What a lovely sight, all the whites dancing and gleaming in the sunny breeze. Many were the times in winter when the washing froze on the lines and was rigid when I unpegged it. If the weather was bad there was only one thing for it and that was to hang it inside. I would hang it on a wooden rack, high up in the kitchen or cellar, which I could lower for access with a rope pulley system. I would also drape it over an upright wooden frame called a clothes maiden or clothes horse. Steam rising around it in the warmth of the kitchen range gave off that lovely fresh laundered smell.

My hands suffered terribly from the soda in the washing and from preparing vegetables. I soon learned to cover them with gloves when I went out. Still, when the washing was done, there was the clearing up to be done and then the upstairs to see to. Bedroom fireplaces to be reset, beds to be made and bedrooms to be tidied. As this house had an inside water closet, I did not have chamber pots to empty. However, I did have wash facilities to clean.

Tuesday was ironing day and all the washing from Monday had to be carefully ironed to get rid of any creases. I had two irons, one on the kitchen range warming up and the other, already heated ready to use. The materials were difficult to iron and had to be at the right level of dampness to get the creases out. With the sheets, it was a bit easier because if they were folded just right before going through the mangle, or if it was blowy on the line, the creases almost disappeared. It gave me such a feeling of satisfaction to see all the clean clothes and sheets tidily ironed and stacked ready to go in the wardrobes. That was that until next Monday.

On other days there was always the sweeping, dusting and polishing. The house got very dusty from the coal fires. Slam the door and a great cloud of smoke would come down the chimney and fill the room. One of the tips Annie gave me was to sprinkle damp tea leaves on the floor before sweeping, as it kept the dust from flying around. Another tip was to clean the windows with newspaper soaked with vinegar and then polish with dry newspapers, so I kept them in a pile in the kitchen when they were finished with. Often, I would read these papers when I had a spare minute or take them to my room if I had time free. It helped to improve my reading and I found it exciting to know what was happening in the world.

I quite liked Mrs Holbrook. She was very patient with me when I first started working without Annie. I usually wore a dark long-sleeved dress with a white collar and a white apron over it whilst I did my work. If Mrs Holbrook had visitors for afternoon tea or dinner and I was serving, I would change my apron for a frilled pinafore and a little lace cap.

Young Mr Charles Holbrook was at sea most of the time. A few years after I started working for them, he married and brought his wife Lena to live in the house. She was only about six or seven years older than me. She seemed quite nervous around Mrs Holbrook for a while but as they got to know each other the running of the house was left to the new Mrs Holbrook. She didn't change any of the routines of the house and liked to cook and bake meals for the household several times a week which I welcomed. Neither ladies were difficult taskmasters and that is the reason I stayed with them for so long.

Sometimes I had a few hours free after my evening chores but mostly I was too tired to do anything except read a book or a few pages from my bible by candlelight and fall asleep before my early morning start. In Winter I never saw my room in daylight. It was dark when I rose and dark when I finished work.

But in the Summer, I was wakened with the rays of the rising sun lighting the room. A bright yellow window shaped square decorated the facing wall even this early in the day. The sun's rays on my homemade glass bead decoration threw dancing lights of happiness around the room. It always cheered me to wake with the sun shining. Listening to the early morning birdsong I would stretch my arms out and enjoy the moment.

On a Sunday I walked to the church with both Mrs Holbrooks and listened with interest to the sermon. All the while watching the other ladies and their maids, taking a keen note of their clothes and style. Hats were very large, gloves were worn and dresses had billowing shoulders and still, some ladies wore their bustles, though corsets didn't appear to be as tightly worn as they had been. With corsets, I could get my waist to eighteen inches but that didn't leave much room to breathe. Stockings were worn with leather ankle boots, buttoned down the side for fasteners.

After Sunday lunch I would travel back to Emsworth by train to see Mama and Pa and the children. It was a lovely time with lots of hugs and kisses. They were all keen to hear tales of the family I worked for and the gossip and news from Portsmouth. They laughed when I told them of mistakes I had made when serving a meal, or mishearing an instruction. I would tell them of my little trips on the electric tram into Portsmouth centre on errands for Mrs Holbrook. They loved to hear of all the new fashions in the shops and what the wealthy people were wearing. Sometimes I was able to tell them I had bumped into girls I knew from Emsworth who were also in service here. Mama was happy that I might have the chance to meet some girls of my own age and not be working in the house all the time. I assured her that I was making lots of friends that I could chat with especially after church on a Sunday. I wrote at least one letter to Mama every week and loved it when Mrs Holbrook picked up the post in the hallway and handed an envelope to me. I would tuck it into my dress pocket and keep it precious all day until I was alone in my room at night. I would light my candle on the chest of drawers and savour every delicate word of Mama's beautiful handwriting.

Chapter Three

1897 saw Queen Victoria's Diamond Jubilee. As part of the celebrations, she came to Portsmouth on 26th June to review her Fleet. Portsmouth was the main port for the Queen's Fleet and the review was to take place on the Solent between Portsmouth and the Isle of Wight. I was sixteen then and because it was such a special occasion Mrs Holbrook told me I could have the whole day off. I travelled home the next Sunday eager to tell my family and ask would they be coming into Portsmouth for the celebrations. They were thrilled that I was free for the day and was told that Mama, Pa, and the family had already decided they were all coming to watch from the shores. Pa was really excited and eagerly showed me the pair of binoculars he was bringing with him for a better view.

With much anticipation and excitement, the day soon came around. The occasion was considered to be of great importance for our naval communities. Everyone in Portsmouth and the surrounding towns had a toe dipped in our naval heritage. Thrilled to honour our wonderful Queen the crowds were dressed in their Sunday best clothes for the day's holiday. Mama had said they were not getting dressed up in their best only to travel on one of Pa's carts, so they came from Emsworth by train to the station at Southsea. I didn't have far to go to meet them.

I stood on the platform at the station and watched the huge engine belching out clouds of smoke and steam as it came to a halt with squealing brakes. Heads poked out of every carriage door ready to jump out. The doors flew open and crowds of hurrying eager people stepped onto the platform. I caught a glimpse of my family halfway along the platform and, bobbing up and down and waving, I waited for them to reach me. Hugging Mama and kissing her soft cheek I immersed myself in her fragrant aroma.

"You look lovely Mama; your dress is new and your hat matches it so well."

Mama had made her new dress herself from soft flowing material, long to her ankles, high at the neck and drawn in tight at the waist. The sleeves were long and full at the top emphasising her shoulders and complementing the wide-brimmed hat decorated with flowers. Her hair was pinned up just showing below the brim and wearing white gloves and carrying a frilly parasol, what a lady she looked. She had also made new clothes for Ann Belle, twelve years old now, and looking quite a stylish young lady too. I glowed with pride as I looked at them. Pa and Henry wore suits with starched white collars and ties. They each wore a straw boater hat with a ribbon decorating it. Young James was almost seven years old now and was dressed in knee-length breeches with a fitted jacket, starched white round collar, black stockings, and buckled shoes and a cap. No more babyish smock tops for him. How he had grown since I left home two years ago. Henry carried a large basket with a cotton cover which Mama said held a wonderful picnic for later. I leaned over it and smelled the aroma of freshly baked bread. A delight to my senses as I remembered how lovely Mama's baking was.

We walked to the promenade and headed towards the castle. Along the front, there was a long sloping grassy bank and we claimed our positions as high up as we could. Not wanting to get grass stains on our new dresses we laid out a thin blanket to sit on. Shouting his wares as he walked the pathway came a hawker armed with so many flags on sticks that we could hardly see him. We all wanted Union Jack flags to wave so we sent James scampering down to him with some money. With a big smile on his face, he came running up the

26

slope waving three flags in each hand, nearly tripping up in his excitement. Everyone was buying them. The flag seller must have made a lot of money that day.

The crowds increased as time moved on and the anticipation grew. Looking out to the Solent we beheld such a spectacle.

One hundred and sixty-five warships were lined up. Five lines of ships, seven miles long. All with tall masts bedecked with flags. White fluffy clouds scuttered across the blue sky as the breeze raised small white tops to the choppy sea. The flags fluttered and as the tide changed, it caused the ships to swing round on their anchors, showing miles of ironclad ships, broadside. Each ship standing out clearly defined in all her majesty of form and jauntiness of colour. Pa was so excited as he scanned the ships with his binoculars, looking for any that he had served on; HMS Duke of Wellington, HMS Asia, HMS Spiteful, HMS Malabar which had been decommissioned the year before. He had served for years on that ship carrying troops back and forth to India. And there in the harbour HMS Victory in all her splendour. He proudly told us of his short time serving on her.

"Did you know that it had been Lord Nelson's flagship at the Battle of Trafalgar in 1805?"

"Yes, Pa. You've told us so many times." We laughed, he was always telling us about the ships. He passed the binoculars around and we could see Her Majesty's Yacht, The Victoria and Albert II, travelling up and down the lines of ships. She was brightly decorated with flags, flying the Royal Standard, the Admiralty Flag, and the British and Union Jack. Each ship as they passed played "God Save The Queen". The sounds carrying over the water. It was played so many times, we just couldn't get it out of our heads for days. Any quiet moment and we realised we were humming it again and again.

We were all cheering at the spectacle and patriotically waving our own little Union Jack flags. So proud were we of our wonderful Queen Victoria and her British Navy. As we watched, a small white steam launch with smoke billowing from her funnel travelled in and out of the fleet at around 34 knots. We thought at first it was a joke but Pa said they were showing off the first steam launch. The Royal Yacht eventually, towards late afternoon, departed taking our Queen back to Osborne House across the water on the Isle of Wight. We sat and ate what was left of our picnic of ham, cheese, homemade bread, apples and Mama's homemade lemonade and ginger beer. We sat and chatted and played with James. Pa had smuggled, in an inside pocket of his jacket, a flask of dark rum. This was his drink of choice after years in the Navy. I smiled to myself. He thought I hadn't seen him as he passed it sneakily to Henry behind Mama's back.

As the festival came to an end and the tired sun began to sink, guns were fired from the ships in tribute and smoke drifted around the masts. Fireworks were sent into the sky from each of the ships creating a riot of colour amongst the haze and echoed reflections in the sea below. It was such a fantastic vision to end such a wonderful day. There was much cheering and clapping from the Southsea banks but we were just a small part of the vast crowds which lined the banks of the Solent that day. I lay in bed that night remembering every delicious little detail of our wonderful day over and over again until my eyes drooped and I fell asleep.

The next day seemed peaceful and quiet after all the celebrating of yesterday. Mr and Mrs Holbrook and his mother had also been rejoicing. They had been to a naval reception for senior officers and their families to celebrate the review and were still in bed. It had been such a beautiful day and as I rose and looked out of my bedroom window there was a soft sea mist veiling the houses as the sun was rising. It held that promise of being a lovely day again. But today I would have a lot of work to catch up with after my day off. It was worth it to have such a magical day with all my family on such a special occasion.

Chapter Four

When we went to church on Sunday I met up with other girls who were in service and while our mistresses were catching up with friends, we discussed our situations. From some of the tales I heard, I was very lucky to be with the Holbrooks. Occasionally girls were not very well treated in the homes or not given the time off that they should have. Being a housemaid was hard work and some girls were just not able to do the jobs they were employed to do and that made them unhappy and insecure. They worried they may be dismissed and there would be no money to send home.

I became friendly with a girl called Alice who was about four years older than me. She was very cheerful and friendly and we got on well. I always looked out for her on a Sunday. Our friendship grew and some Sundays during the summertime, when I didn't always want to travel home to Emsworth, we would meet up and take a stroll along Clarence Esplanade or South Parade Pier. As Sunday afternoon was the time most servants were allowed time off, we often met up with groups of girls we were acquainted with.

When the weather was warm it was usual for families to take their children for a day out at the beach. There were bathing huts lined up along the shore for ladies to change from their dresses into a bathing costume, which still covered most of their bodies and legs, and a swimming cap. As a young lady it was not done to be seen, shoes and stockings off, paddling in the sea. But it was the thing to be seen parading along the promenade in your best clothes.

We strolled along, arm in arm, under frilly parasols in twos and threes laughing and chatting. Always we had an eye out for any young men we wished to impress. Always there were plenty of sailors in their uniforms taking a stroll. Sometimes

31

the soldiers from the Garrison or the Hilsea Barracks came to Southsea for a day out. Sailors whose ships were in port. Some from foreign lands. We laughed when they tried to talk to us because we couldn't understand a word they were saying. If they liked you, they sometimes asked if they may walk alongside you and your friends and introduce themselves. We had such fun giggling and flirting with them. We were never short of young men. Young men, who were being sent once again to another Boer War in South Africa, enjoying themselves before they went. The turn of the century saw a very busy Portsmouth harbour with troop ships toing and froing to South Africa.

On 22nd January 1901, only four years on from the grand spectacle we had witnessed, for Queen Victoria's Diamond Jubilee, the country was saddened to hear that she had passed away at Osborne House on the Isle of Wight. The country was grieving the loss of such a great queen as she had been. She had reigned for 60 years. So long that most of us could not remember a time without her. Portsmouth went into mourning. Dark clothes were worn and black flags hung in shop windows. Union Jack flags hung at half-mast from the buildings.

On 1st February in Portsmouth, we mourned our Queen in our nautical way. The Royal Yacht Alberta, lying at Trinity Pier near to Osborne House, received the body of Queen Victoria which was solemnly brought aboard and laid in the saloon. Slowly as it sailed across the Spithead Anchorage we listened to the sombre firing of minute guns from the Royal Navy and foreign warships which were anchored there. We could hear the guns all over town, boom after boom, boom after boom. A sad subdued mood draped itself over the people of Portsmouth as the town came to a standstill. This naval city had loved its Queen. Those who could lined the shores but in town, the sound was stopping people in their tracks. As it neared the land, the shore batteries took up the doleful salute. She was then taken from Gosport to be laid to rest in the Royal Mausoleum at Windsor alongside her beloved husband Prince Albert. A hushed solemnness hung over us for several days. We all shared stories of her reign and the celebrations we had seen at Portsmouth. We were seafaring families in Portsmouth who had loved to serve our Queen.

Now it was God Save The King. Victoria's son Albert, heir to the throne, had become King Edward V11. Albert had been Prince of Wales for longer than any of his predecessors. He had travelled the country and the Commonwealth performing ceremonial duties for Victoria and was very popular among the fashionable leisured elite. It was rumoured that his mother had thought him a bit of a playboy. But no matter what she thought he was now our King and we all hoped he would be a good King. His coronation would not take place until 1902, after a year of mourning.

It was in 1901 that the Boer War in South Africa came to an end and once again we received back war-torn young men. Sailors and soldiers alike, all looking for relief from the battles abroad. The soldiers were rehabilitated in Hilsea Barracks, convalescing in the clean sea air of Portsmouth before returning to their bases.

Eager to meet young ladies they visited the promenades once again in Southsea and it was here one Sunday afternoon when walking with Alice that we met a group of young soldiers who had just returned from South Africa. One young man stood out. He was so charming with his dark brown twinkling eyes, curly black hair and an infectious grin. He introduced himself as Harry and asked, in a charming Irish accent, if they may walk with us. He walked next to me and I could hardly dare to lift my eyes to look at him. We giggled as they joked with us and bantered with each other, showing off for our attention. He flattered me saying how beautiful he thought I was and before we knew it, it was time to part. How fast the time goes when you are so engrossed in the moment. I was absolutely smitten and with Alice, we agreed to meet them again the following Sunday. How strange this feeling. I had never felt like this with any of the other young men we had met. Was it his eyes, his lilting Irish chatter, his attentiveness? We never really know why do we. We just know when they are the right one.

My stomach churned all week and I could hardly concentrate on my work. I would have to do something with my hands to make them look more respectable if I took off a glove. They were red and dry from the carbolic soap and soda and peeling vegetables. I saved the lemon skins in the kitchen and every night I rubbed the skins on my hands then coated them in glycerine overnight. I washed my hair with lye soap and warm water and rinsed it well. I rinsed it with vinegar water to make it shine. Every night I let my hair down and vigorously brushed it one hundred times to make it look healthy. Every night I lay in bed thinking of those dark brown eyes that twinkled when I looked at him and the enchanting accent when he spoke. Oh, I thought would Sunday never arrive. I checked my Sunday outfit was especially clean and my Sunday boots had a high polish. By Saturday night my hands were looking a lot better and my gloves were laundered to perfection. Would he be there to meet us or would I be sadly disappointed?

Sunday arrived and the weather was fine. I looked at the sky anxiously hoping it would stay sunny so I didn't have to cover my best outfit. I couldn't concentrate at church and found myself daydreaming of Harry whilst I should have been listening to the sermon. After lunch, which I only pecked at,

I went upstairs and dressed. I brushed my hair again, pinned it up and, put my hat on, holding it in place with a hatpin. I looked at myself in the mirror, pinched my cheeks and, bit my lips to raise a bit of colour. Putting my clean white gloves on, off I went. As I stepped out, I realised in my haste I had left my parasol behind and had to nip back in for it. Alice met me at the usual place and we walked nervously towards the promenade. We had often met young men to walk with but I had never felt like this about anyone. Alice laughed and teased me but said not to worry she was sure he would be there. My stomach was doing somersaults. As we reached the promenade, we saw Harry and his friend sauntering up and down looking for us. I needn't have worried about bringing colour to my cheeks and lips. I felt my whole face blushing.

Walking in couples, Harry and myself, Alice and her young man, we strolled along towards Clarence Esplanade. Harry was such a gentleman but so friendly and easy to talk to. He asked about my family and told me about his family up in Manchester. All that I had heard of Manchester was that it was a large smoky industrial city up in the north with lots of cotton mills.

Harry had two brothers, Patrick who was a coal miner in Wigan, John (Jack) who was a carter, and four sisters; Mary was a pupil teacher, Kathleen (Kitty) was a machinist, Helena (Lena) and Bridget whom they called Delia were still in school. They had all been born in Clonmel in Ireland. His parents had been in service at Marlfield House until they married. His father had then taken a smallholding in Whitefort and over the years had tried to support his family. When times became too difficult, he had travelled to America in search of work and after a short time they had been informed that he had died there. After that their mother Ellen had brought the family to Manchester. She had a sister who was settled in Hulme, who told her there was plenty of work there. He spoke of them as a large very happy Irish family who all worked very hard to support themselves.

The afternoon went so fast that it was soon time to leave his company and return to Allens Road. As we said goodbye I waited anxiously until he asked could we meet again.

Oh yes. "I would love to." I rather coyly agreed.

We spent many Sunday afternoons walking the promenades, or the seashore, tasting the cockles, winkles and, mussels, spoilt for choice by the numerous seafood vendors along the shore. I loved being near the sea. I always felt free and energised. The air was always so clean and salty. The sound of the sea was exhilarating as it sometimes thundered onto the shore when it was windy and the tide was high. The seagulls rising and soaring on the breeze. If the weather was not so good Harry would take me to the refreshment rooms at South Parade Pier where we would sit and drink tea from china cups served by waitresses in black dresses, starched frilly aprons, and frilled caps. It was a real treat for me to be served by someone else. I loved it and it made Harry smile. He said I looked like a lady and should be treated as such.

Several times as we walked along by the Canoe Lake, when the weather was warm, we hired a rowing boat and I sat grandly at one end with my parasol protecting me from the sun. Harry would show his skills with the oars and as he propelled us from one end to the other, I would peep flirtatiously at him from under the frill of my parasol. On occasion, we would take the new electric tram into the centre of Portsea and walk around looking in the shop windows and after much persuasion from Harry, we occasionally went into a public house. I didn't like going there. They were always dark inside and smelled of stale beer and tobacco smoke. Some of the women in there were rather raucous and I was really out of my depth but Harry kept me close and made me feel comfortable. I sometimes had a glass of stout or a gin. I only ever had one as I couldn't be seen to be tipsy when I returned to Allens Road. Harry would have a couple of pints of beer as he was used to drinking with his soldier friends. We always had such a lovely time, never running out of things to talk about. Our lives were so different and we learned so much about each other on those afternoons.

Occasionally after we had been meeting for a long time, I took Harry to meet Mama and Pa. I had written in my letters that I was meeting Harry on Sundays and that was why I hadn't been home as much. She had replied that they were all looking forward to meeting him. Would it be soon?

Mama was charmed by him and welcomed him into our home. The family all crowded in to meet him. When they found out he was a soldier James had lots to ask him about the Boer War and South Africa. But Pa held back a bit and quietly observed him. He had already noted his Irish accent. There were a lot of bad political feelings about the Irish Catholics around that time and I hadn't thought about that before I brought him home. We were all Church of England. He was also a soldier and that didn't go down very well with a Navy man. Harry recognised how Pa was feeling and didn't feel very comfortable with him but he was polite and well-mannered, and never gave Pa anything else to hold against him. I must admit I was so in love with him by then that I thought it was bad of Pa to feel like that. But this would have been the way most people were feeling. I didn't take him home on too many occasions to avoid any bad feelings.

Eventually, Harry was transferred from Hilsea Barracks to the Royal Artillery Headquarters in Larkhill, Wiltshire. We were both devastated by this move and agreed to write to each other. We wrote as often as we could and he travelled to

Portsmouth by train whenever he got a day's leave. One Sunday afternoon as we walked, Harry took my hand and asked if I would marry him. With no hesitation, I said yes. I was overjoyed to think of us being married but couldn't think how it would be possible and where we would live. The only plan we could think would work out was for him to leave the army and get another job. Then we could get married.

We knew my Pa's views on Harry's background so it was with trepidation that we went to Emsworth. As I was over twenty-one we didn't legally need my parents' permission but Harry came to my home with me and asked Pa for my hand in marriage. Pa said he did not approve because of the difference in backgrounds and that if we married, he would not come to the wedding. Mama was very upset for us but could not and would not go against Pa. We left the house disappointed and went back to Portsmouth both very upset and wondering what to do. Poor Harry felt insulted to think my family thought he wasn't good enough. The sympathetic sky was dark and it rained heavily on the journey back seeming to echo our emotions. We should have realised this could happen and I felt angry with Pa and so embarrassed for Harry. I was in turmoil. I now had to choose to marry Harry or listen to my Pa. We left each other that day, both in confusion, but deeply in love.

I met up the next weekend with Alice in a local park where we could have a bit of privacy and poured my heart out to her. She hugged me and listened to all I told her through anger and disappointment and tears. She helped me so much in deciding what I should do but never took sides either with my parents or Harry. I owe a lot to Alice.

It was 1906 and before we made any decisions, Harry was urgently called home from the army as his brother Patrick had been killed in a coal mining accident in Wigan. Amidst all the sorrow with his family, plans were made. He told his Mother of his wish to marry me and what had happened with my family. At first, she was disappointed that I was not a Catholic but she asked him to find out if I was willing to become a Catholic. That came as a surprise to me and I wasn't sure what I thought about it. Was this the only way we could be together? What was I to do? I said that I would think about it but I needed to know all about being a Catholic first. With this reply, Harry's Mother helped him to put the wheels in motion.

Harry gave notice and left the army, although he would have to stay on the army books as a reservist. This was a new army rule brought into being to make sure that if a war broke out again, they would always have more trained soldiers ready to call back into action. He went to work in Manchester. He got a job with the Lancashire and Yorkshire Railway Company as a Goods Porter near Exchange Station just into Salford over the River Irwell. This was physical work but as a soldier, he was physically fit. Harry's Mother went all out to help us and found a place of work for me in a household in Bowdon near Manchester. This was a big step for me and I walked up and down the promenade with Alice trying to decide what to do. I desperately wanted to be with Harry and get married but on the other hand, I would be going against my parents. After much heartache, I decided to go to Manchester.

The next Sunday I went to Emsworth to face my parents with the decision I had made. Pa said he was very sorry it had come to this and although he loved me very much, he just could not attend a wedding to an Irish Catholic soldier. He liked Harry but it was his background he couldn't come to terms with. He thought I would not fit into an Irish Catholic environment. He said he had heard such terrible things about

Catholics and the Irish people. Henry was in much the same mind as Pa but James was too young to realise the politics and implications of it all. Ann Belle tried to be helpful and said she would have done the same in my shoes but she wasn't in my shoes was she? Poor Mama was distraught but could not disagree with Pa. Mama and I had a very emotional goodbye but none of us fell out over it. It was just the way it was, and it would not change.

I was on my own now to follow my heart. I promised to write to them and let them know my address, and to tell them about my position in the house in Bowdon and when my wedding was to be. The sky was darkening and a fine drizzle dampened my clothes as I arrived back at Allens Road. With drooping shoulders but a brave heart, I asked young Mrs Holbrook if I could speak with her on Monday. I explained my position and what I was hoping to do. She was so kind, she understood how much I was in love with my Harry and how hard it must have been for me to make these decisions. She agreed to me leaving at the end of the week and gave me an excellent reference. The older Mrs Holbrook said she was very sorry to see me go and would miss me but wished me a good life with Harry. How nice that was of her.

To confirm my decision, I went and bought a single train ticket to Manchester. One single ticket to Manchester. It was the end of one chapter and the start of the next. I had done it now. It was happening soon and although it would have been most unladylike, I almost skipped home to Allens Road to start packing my case.

Chapter Five

It was a long journey from Portsmouth to Manchester. My seat was in an eight-seater carriage with a corridor along one side. It wasn't very busy so I mostly had the carriage to myself as people got on and off at different stations along the way. I felt very important and independent, although a bit nervous, doing this on my own. There was no going back now. I only knew what I had been told about the North and wondered if it would match the picture in my mind. But all that would be immaterial really because the most important and exciting thing was being back with Harry again. I sat by the window, eating my sandwiches, watching the ever-changing scenery as we went through towns and villages. Passing farms and fields, lambs, sheep, herds of cows lifting their heads as we rumbled by.

A gentleman in a suit, sitting almost opposite, sat and read his newspaper for the whole of his journey never glancing up at any fellow travellers. I wasn't sure if it was acceptable to strike up conversations with fellow passengers but when a mother and her three young children entered my carriage near Birmingham, I didn't have much choice. Such a friendly lady who told me almost her whole life story immediately although I found it quite difficult to understand her accent. Her children sat quietly at first but as they started to get bored, I noticed them giving little elbow digs to wind each other up. What a good job they weren't travelling the whole way like myself.

It had started to get a bit stuffy in the carriage so I let the window down a bit to enjoy the lovely country air but was rewarded with smuts of soot and the smoke from the engine so I hurriedly lifted the window and fastened it with the big leather strap on the brass hook.

I could almost tell that we were nearing Manchester as the sky became darker. The colour of the houses started to change from creamy stone colour to red brick. And then as the train was almost arriving at London Road Station in Manchester, I felt I had never seen anything so dark and dismal in my life. The clean fresh air of the open countryside was left behind. Everywhere were six and seven-storey buildings with tall chimneys belching out plumes of black smoke. The bricks of the buildings were almost black. The streets looked damp and dirty.

The train pulled in and the station was filled with the smoke and steam from the engines. Managing to lift my suitcase onto the platform, I looked earnestly through the crowds and spotted Harry coming towards me in his best suit and waving his cap in the air. That wonderful smile on his face and the magic twinkle in his eyes. We fell into each other and hugged, totally oblivious of the crowds of passengers and porters around us. His warm masculine aroma thrilled me. His strong arms held me. After all our letters I was so delighted to be with him. It had been so long since I last saw him. Thank goodness I had taken the chance and followed my heart.

We walked out of the station and along towards the Manchester Royal Infirmary in Piccadilly. Immediately I tasted the grimy smoke in my mouth. Where was the clean salty air of Southsea? The buildings were black with soot, the ground was muddy and I managed to keep my hem from the floor but couldn't do much to keep the shine on my boots except try to sidestep the puddles. I was surprised by the number of people sitting around outside the Infirmary looking ragged and poor. Harry said they were unemployed with nowhere to go. There was so much hustle and bustle everywhere. So many horses and carts, horse-drawn buses and, electric trams hurrying in all directions. There appeared to be no order in this mayhem. People seemed to have no care for their lives which could be taken from them as they dashed to cross the traffic avoiding the steaming heaps left by the horses. From here we caught an electric tram to Moss Side. The people we passed all seemed careworn and poor, the women wearing shawls covering their heads, bent with worries. So different from those at home. Harry said they worked mostly in the mills working long hours for not much money. Their homes were very basic and small and accommodated large families, very overcrowded with people even renting spaces in the cellars and attics. Sanitary arrangements were even worse; the whole street sharing one or two privies.

As we reached Moss Side we were greeted with row after row of bay-windowed terraced houses, black with soot, their chimneys emitting clouds of smoke from coal fires. The streets were cobbled and gas lights stood at intervals along the flagged pavements. It was not as poor an area as the others we had travelled through. These houses had cellars and attics. Some had three steps up to the front door, some had small enclosed gardens at the front. All had walled backyards with an outside toilet. At the back between the rows of houses were entries, or ginnels as they called them; narrow cobbled passageways for entry by the backyard doors.

We arrived at Meadow Street. Harry carrying my case, and holding my hand. Good job I had gloves on, my hands were getting sweaty. My heart was beating ten to the dozen. I wondered what his family would be like and what they would think of me. Maybe I had been a bit reckless in thinking they would accept me. They knew I wasn't a Catholic.

Harry's mother opened the door before we could knock. She must have been peeping out from her net curtains to see us coming along the street. She was a buxom lady with a smiling homely face. Her hair was dark and pinned up in the fashion of the day. She couldn't have been more welcoming. She greeted me with a hug and a kiss on my cheek. She took us into the living room and made a cup of tea with a slice of cake for us. We chatted for quite a time over our cups of tea. Her Irish accent was difficult for me to understand at first as it was a lot stronger than Harry's. I was careful to drink from my cup but Mrs Curran was happy to pour her hot tea into the saucer and drink from there. I usually drank from the saucer at home but not where I might be judged. I was to meet some more of Harry's family later when they came home from work. Harry took my bag and showed me to a bedroom upstairs which I was to share with his sisters until I went to my new employment in Bowdon.

I met them all over the evening meal when we were served with an abundance of meat and vegetables, buttered soda bread, followed by a sweet suet pudding. I was asked so many questions about Portsmouth, my family, the train journey, my friends. They talked so fast and all had that lilting Irish accent. They were joyous. After the meal, we were all invited to join in a celebratory drink; gin, stout, homemade lemonade. They were such a loving happy family I knew I would be happy with them. Mrs Curran was definitely in charge and before I went to my new place of work in Bowdon, where I would live until we married, I was taken to meet Fr Rowan at English Martyrs Catholic Church. My first impressions of him were what a lovely welcoming priest.

It was arranged that I should meet with the nuns at Loreto Convent for my instructions about becoming a Catholic. I duly went along and met Sister Andrea. She was a very softly spoken lady whose whole demeanour spoke of her love of God. Over several months and building on what I already knew from my churchgoings, she gave me such a love of God that I was happy to become a Catholic and at English Martyrs Church I was received, by Fr James Rowan, into the Faith. Like many Irish families, this was another excuse for a party with plenty of food and a few drinks. Goodness me, this family made me so welcome. They loved the fact that Harry had found himself a girlfriend to marry.

His mother worked as a Monthly Nurse looking after new mothers and their babies until the mother was up and about. It was advised that new mothers stay in bed for a month after giving birth. Only those with wealth could afford this luxury. Wives and mothers who were not so well off were up and about their housework the next day. Through her work, she had gotten to know quite a few prosperous families and their servants, and that was how she found a position for me in Bowdon eleven miles south of Manchester.

The houses in Bowdon were very large and each stood in their own grounds. These belonged to families with money, most of which had been made from the cotton trade. Many factory owners lived here because the smoke from their factories never reached this far. I was not the only maid as they employed quite a number in each house. I don't know if it was because they didn't want their lines of laundry spoiling the look of the gardens but a lot of the laundry was sent out to be done in Bowdon Vale down the hill. It was nicknamed "Soapy Town" for this reason. At the top of the hill where we were, the area was very leafy. Everywhere, in gardens and along the roads, there were large established elm trees. The roads were fairly quiet until you reached the thoroughfare into the market town of Altrincham.

When I had my time off, I would walk from Bowdon into Altrincham and get the train from there to meet Harry. He would take me to Loreto Convent for my lessons with Sister

Andrea. The convent, surrounded by streets of terraced houses, was behind a tall brick wall but when you went through the gate, they had a delightful garden full of flower beds. No wonder the nuns walked around the garden paths saying their Rosary. Inside the big wooden front door, I was greeted with the overwhelming smell of beeswax from the dark wooden panelling and staircase that was always polished to perfection. I never went in there without seeing a nun going up and down with a duster polishing and polishing. I wondered did she pray all the time she was doing it. Or perhaps she was dreaming of home. The small chapel in the convent was the most beautiful I have ever seen. It was filled with dark polished wood, an ornate altar and large stained glass windows either side of the altar. After my lessons, I would go and have a meal with Harry's family before travelling back to Bowdon in the evening.

I wrote home frequently telling them all my news and the plans for the wedding. Mama wrote telling me that James was working as a driver in Portsmouth Dockyard where he was very happy. Pa and Henry were changing the business to using a lorry and a van instead of the horse-drawn cart and had taught James to drive. Sadly, there had not been enough work in the family haulage business to employ him as well. Mama sent parcels to me of things I would need in my own home; tablecloths, antimacassars, tray cloths and, suchlike which she had embroidered herself. She also sent me new petticoats and stockings. As the time of the wedding drew near, I longed for them to be with me on my special day. I asked again if they would please come to see me wed but Mama said that Pa was unfortunately not a healthy man at the time and was unable to travel the distance. She would need to be with him. It hit me all over again; their feelings towards Harry and how much I was homesick. There was only one consolation given to me and that was that my darling little brother, who was now twenty, would be allowed to come to Manchester on their behalf. What joy, James would be able to walk me down the aisle and give me away in place of Pa. Such small joy, but it was a comfort.

Mrs Curran and Harry's sisters were more than helpful in preparing everything for our wedding. As I was new around here, I was glad of the help but couldn't help thinking it would have been nice for Mama to be helping me. As the day of the wedding drew near I left my position in Bowdon and moved back into the house with Harry's sisters. My wedding dress had been made by a local seamstress and I went with Harry's sister Mary to buy a hat to go with it. I selected a large-brimmed circular hat about three inches tall which stood on the crown of my head allowing some of my hair to be shown. I also bought a pair of new white shoes. Mama had sent me new white gloves and stockings. Mary was such a help. Her teaching skills made her so organised. As I had no family here, the guest list included Harry's direct family and Mrs Curran's sister Catherine Mather's family. The bridesmaids and page boys were to be all the Mather children. My brother, James Brockway, and Harry's sister, Mary Curran were to act as witnesses to our marriage.

On 22nd May 1907 I rose early as I was so excited and nervous. Harry and his brother had stayed elsewhere for the night so as not to see the bride on her wedding day. That really would have been bad luck. We ate a good hearty Irish breakfast, although I was too nervous to eat much. We girls commandeered the bedroom for ourselves and after bathing, in the metal bathtub, taken down from where it hung on the wall outside, Mary helped me to dress ready for the marriage. She was as excited as I was and we laughed and chattered away as she gently brushed my hair coaxing and pinning it into a smart style to go under my hat. We would be coming back to the house for our celebration meal so Mrs Curran and the other sisters were all busy in the kitchen. Irish parties require lots and lots of food and drink. Mrs Curran had also been in service before she was married in Clonmel so she knew how things should be done.

James arrived at the house in his best suit and starched white collar. I was overjoyed to see him. It was lovely to see his eyes light up when he saw me in my wedding dress. I could tell he was proud of me. Mrs Curran gave us both a glass of sherry, "to steady the nerves."

We had hired a pony and trap to take us to church and after the bridesmaids and Mrs Curran had been taken first to wait at church it returned for us. James took my hand and helped me up the step then joined me. How grand I felt lighting the drab streets with my glowing joy. Heads turned and wished us good luck as the horse clopped along on the cobbles. James held my hand and shared with me how proud Mama and Pa would have been to see me now. He was so glad he had taken the opportunity of coming to Manchester and seeing how happy we both were. It surprised him that I had settled so well in this dark smoky town which was so different from where I had grown up but did agree that love conquers all.

I heard the melodious, church filling, sound of the organ as it began to play the Bridal Chorus. I tried to remember not to rush down the aisle but step steadily with my arm in James' arm. I knew all smiling eyes were on me but I only looked straight ahead to see Harry waiting for me. I hardly remember the wedding ceremony as I was so overawed by the grandeur of English Martyrs, the swelling sound of the harmonising organ pipes filling the vast church, the number of people there to watch us and Fr Rowan celebrating the marriage. But most of all that wonderful smile on Harry's face as I came up the aisle. He stood there in his new suit and waistcoat, starched white collar, his pocket watch hanging on a gold Albert chain in his waistcoat pocket.

What a glorious day. "I do," "I do," "Oh yes I do!"

Joyously we left the church arm in arm to the grand sounds of the Wedding March.   At the door, happy onlookers showered us with confetti and rice. We were bombarded with congratulatory kisses and hugs. Such a profusion of joy and happiness. I was now Mrs Curran, proud wife of the most handsome man around.

Back at the house, we all positioned ourselves in three rows on the pavement outside the front window whilst we had photographs taken. The photographer stood in the middle of the cobbled street, behind his tripod with his head under a dark piece of material peering at the scene through the lens until we were all ready. We all had to keep very still while it was taken, so it was easier to keep a straight face instead of trying to hold a smile, or the picture would have been blurred.

The celebrations were joyful with plates and plates of meats and cheeses and soda bread, and a very large pan of Irish stew. Cakes and pies were served afterwards and all the time the drinks flowed in large measures. Speeches were made to welcome me into the family and a few tales told to embarrass Harry.   I laughed and relaxed in this lovely company. They all accepted me as part of their large family. "Mrs Curran" was laughingly called out a few times to see if I turned my head at my new name. A fiddler started the music and an evening of singing began; sad ballads, raucous Irish rebel songs and, drinking songs that got everyone singing. What a wonderful family they were.

James and I were amazed at all the celebrations and both laughingly thought that with all this Irish patriotism, it was perhaps better Pa hadn't come after all. James said he didn't think that Pa was a fit man and thought the journey would have been too much for him. He was struggling to get about now as his breathing was laboured and he soon got tired. He promised to tell them all, especially Mama, how happy I was and what a good day it had been. I am sure that Pa secretly wished he could have walked me down the aisle and seen me in my wedding dress but he had his principles and he had stuck by them. I would send some photographs back with James and some of our wedding cake, which had been made with lots of dried fruit soaked in good Irish Guinness. I laughed to think Pa would at least have to thank the Irish for that.

Chapter Six

We started our married life taking a room as lodgers in a house on Platt Street. I wasn't able to be employed as a servant now since I was married so I tried to fill my time with cleaning and baking for Harry. I went to church and visited the nuns at the convent. If I had any company I liked to go and watch the ladies bowling teams in Alexandra Park. I met some lovely people there. Mrs Frost, who went to English Martyrs Church and played bowls, was also newly married with time on her hands. She proved to be a very dear friend to me over the years.

On a free Sunday afternoon, Harry would walk with me to Alexandra Park and we would proudly stroll, arm in arm, along the Terrace as we had done in Southsea on the seafront. The flower beds, either side of the Terrace, were resplendent with colour in Summer. Lime Walk, as it was aptly named, paraded tall lime trees either side of the wide dappled shady path. Such a lovely walk with my Harry, never short of a conversation and so much in love.

There was much to do and see in this park. It had been a public park since the mid-1800s when Manchester City Council had bought the land from Lord Egerton. They had hoped that it would be so inviting that men would spend their leisure time there instead of the alehouses. It was certainly working for Harry then, but probably only as we were newly married. We strolled around the low metal decorative fence protecting the lake, watching the elegant white swans glide smoothly over the surface, with hardly a ripple, followed by a brood of dull brown feathered cygnets nearly as large as their parents. They always brought to my mind the Hans Christian Anderson story of the ugly duckling. Next year we would be graced with so many graceful, gliding white swans.

I was told that in a really cold winter the lake sometimes froze over and people would go skating on the ice. I had never done that in Southsea and I looked forward to having a try the next winter. Depending on the weather we would occasionally go to the refreshment pavilion for a pot of tea or sit on the deckchairs around the bandstand and listen to the brass band playing. If the weather was cool, there was always the newly opened glass cactus house, which was lovely and warm all the time. I was amazed to see the variety of cacti. Some even had bright red flowers on them but all were very spiky.

Other times I would visit Mrs Curran and my sisters-in-law whilst Harry met up with his friends in one of the public houses. This was new to me. Pa had never gone out drinking with his friends. He had always stayed at home. Here men tended to gather in different pubs with their own kind. For example, carpenters favoured one pub, plumbers another, so if you needed work you had an idea which pub to go in to meet the right people. Harry no doubt went to the one which was favoured by the Irish immigrants. There were a lot of Irish around Moss Side and Hulme. There were also several areas all around Manchester where they gathered; Angel Meadows, New Cross, Ancoats, and many others. This area was a bit better off than the others in North Manchester. Angel Meadows had been a brutal and dirty slum over near the River Irwell, not far from Harry's place of work.

I liked to spend time getting to know his sisters. Mary was always bringing books for me as she knew I liked to read. Kitty, Lena, and Delia did a lot of home dressmaking. They were always offering to make me a new dress as the fashions changed. Being brought up in the Irish countryside, and even though they had each other, they knew what it was like to come to a strange place and they helped me a lot with settling in and making friends. As children, they had lived in the country in Ireland on a smallholding where their father had kept a few animals. They laughed as they told me he had been in trouble with the law for frequently letting his animals roam into his neighbour's field. I wondered had he been too lazy to mend his fence or could he not resist feeding his animals for free. Since his death, it was through their mother's sheer hard work and determination that they had done as well as they had here.

Soon we were able to rent a house of our own at 104 George Street, just behind Platt Street. We had to rely on Harry's wages and any bits of cleaning, washing or, mending that Mrs Curran was able to find for me from the big houses nearby. I loved having our own house to look after. To manage my own home after keeping house for other people for so long was a dream. I was an expert at it. Having worked in big houses I knew how to do everything and I soon had the house spic and span, and "shipshape" as my Pa would have said. Up here in the North proof of good housekeeping was in the pride a housewife took in "donkey stoning" her front step. We had three stone steps outside the front door and every morning the stone flags of the pavement were swept and swilled. Steps were washed to remove the greasy grime which settled from all the soot in the air.

The donkey stones were made of a mixture of pulverised stone, cement, bleach powder and, water. It was mixed and formed into a slab that was cut up into individual stones, suitable to be held in your hand, and laid out to dry. They were first used in the textile mills to clean the greasy steps. You could get three different colours, depending on where they were made, brown, white, and cream. The stone was wetted and then rubbed on the steps and left to dry. If you were very artistic you could use more than one colour and decorate the steps with a pattern or edge. Woe betides anyone who put their dirty boot print on it. This was a daily ritual and a chance for the housewives in their overalls to have a hobnob and gossip as they knelt bent over their steps. A row of overalled bottoms facing the street.

Not all women were content to just be housewives. They wanted to vote like the men, to have a say in everything that was going on, and to have equal rights to men. I liked to read the newspapers and I found that in and around Manchester there was a lot of support for the suffrage movement. Emmeline Goulden, who had been born in Moss Side had married Richard Pankhurst, a lawyer, and supporter of the women's suffrage movement. In 1903 she had helped to found the more militant Women's Social and Political Union. Being quite an independent person myself, I could understand how they might feel but I would never have joined in any demonstrations with them.

Four months since we married, and I found to my great delight that I was going to have a baby. Harry and his family were delighted. This would be the first grandchild and niece or nephew. I wrote immediately to Mama with the news that she would be a Grandma and Pa a Grandad. They wrote back straight away saying how thrilled they were. Mama said she would start knitting baby clothes for me. I also got out my knitting needles and set to on a layette. Harry's sisters, once again came in very handy as machinists and started sewing little cotton nightdresses, dresses, frilled bonnets, pillowcases and, pram covers. They obviously couldn't make anything else until we knew whether it was a boy or girl. I got lots of advice from Mrs Curran and her friends on how to keep myself healthy and active whilst also warning me about things I shouldn't do like raise my arms above my head when hanging out the washing as that could strangle the baby with the umbilical cord, and avoid going near any cats as it can harm the baby. And guessing games started about the shape of my stomach. If you were carrying the baby low, it would be a boy and high, a girl.

Harry was wonderful. He insisted I didn't lift anything heavy or move any furniture around as it was too heavy. As we sat by the fireside in the evening, he encouraged me to have a drink of stout every day to build me up. He would pop along to the corner shop with a jug to be filled by the shopkeeper and of course, there was always enough for both of us. He made sure that I rested with my feet up as they tended to swell up a bit. But I took that opportunity when sitting down, to catch up with mending clothes and darning the holes worn in socks and stockings. Stretching the hole over a wooden darning mushroom, with a darning needle, I wove woollen threads in and out until the hole had been filled.

As it turned out I was huge and surprised everyone, including myself, by giving birth to identical twin girls on 22nd May 1908. Eileen and Kathleen were beautiful little girls with dark hair and brown eyes. Harry was so proud and spent a lot of time wetting the babies' heads with his friends. Mrs Curran came every day to help me. It was so reassuring to see how efficient she was. After all, this was her job and she was a great help to me. It's surprising how one's motherly instincts kick in and I found myself perfectly able to cope with two babies at once. It was double the work but also double the rewards. Eileen and Kathleen were baptised at English Martyrs Church within 10 days as was the religious custom. And of course, we had another excuse for a party.

As they grew, I made the most of the summer weather and proudly pushed my big Silver Cross twin pram, a baby either end with frilled bonnets and pillowcases and covers, up and down Princess Road, Alexandra Road and Withington Road doing my shopping, soaking up all the admiration for my beautiful girls. And of course, around the park on Sundays. But there was a deep sadness within me at that time.

Just five weeks after Eileen and Kathleen were born, I received a letter from Emsworth telling me that Pa had passed away on 30th June, at the age of sixty-two, from heart failure. Mama and James had been right about Pa's health. His difficulties had worsened and his heart had finally given up. I wasn't able to be at Pa's funeral as I was breastfeeding the twins myself and couldn't travel all that way with them. He was buried in Warblington Cemetery along the coastal lane from Emsworth.

He never saw how happy Harry had made me. He never saw my beautiful girls. I never got to hug him for one last time. I missed my Pa so much. I knew that even though he didn't attend my wedding he never thought any the less of me for marrying Harry. I think he was quietly proud of me for standing up for myself and following my heart, my heart which almost broke in two when I heard he had died. I had to hold myself together for the sake of the twins.

Mama was too upset to manage things herself so as soon as I was able, I travelled by train to Emsworth to help her apply for probate over Pa's affairs. Henry was too busy with the business and James was working at the dockyard. Ann Belle had met a young man called Mr Brock and they were both enjoying too much of the "good life" so I couldn't rely on her to organise things. At the time, Pa's brother was in America. He had been a stevedore in the docks and had taken the opportunity of travelling there. He had met a lovely lady called Kate, married her and settled in Pennsylvania. He was still working and was unable to make such a long journey in time for the funeral.

I couldn't stay too long but I made the most of every moment with Mama who was grieving terribly for Pa. She had had to nurse him at home for several months before he died. I asked her to come out with me several times. We strolled down to the harbour and sat by the sea in the sunshine. How I had missed this. We just sat on the bench in the Summer sunshine quietly watching the slow rhythmical flowing on the waves which, bobbed the fishing boats up and down as they approached the shore. The sunlight glinting on the water bringing sparkle into our hearts. We tenderly talked about Pa's love for the sea and the times he had shared his stories with us. We ended up laughing as we remembered some of his stories and our stories of him. Then with a new warmth around us, we strolled home with the sound of the sea behind us.

Probate was granted to Mama and me on 26th August that year. Pa had left the sum of £3,140.9s.3d. which included the house and the business.

By the summer of the next year, I became pregnant again. It was hard work looking after our girls and a house. I wasn't able to take on any casual cleaning work so we took in a boarder to help make ends meet. Molly Flynn was twenty and came from Clonmel to work as a restaurant waitress in Manchester City Centre. The extra money came in handy even though I was expected to cook meals for her. She had the attic room at the top of the house and the girls were in their cots in the back bedroom.

After a quiet family Christmas, I had a letter from Uncle Henry and Auntie Kate telling us they would be arriving in England on 25th January 1910 and looked forward to calling on us. They sailed the Atlantic from New York to Liverpool on the Lusitania, a British Ocean Liner, and stayed in a hotel in Manchester. They came laden with presents for us and the girls. I didn't know Uncle Henry well having only seen him when I was very young. Auntie Kate was charming and very easy to talk to. Uncle Henry had retired and was visiting Portsmouth with views to settling back in England. I was thrilled as they would be welcomed company for Mama. From Manchester, they travelled by train with all their trunks to Portsmouth. I had several letters from Mama and Kate over the next year telling me all about how they were buying a house and settling in Portsmouth.

A month later on 21st February 1910, a cold Monday in the middle of a smoggy Manchester winter, George Henry Curran arrived into the world. A son and heir to carry on the family name gave the family another excuse to rejoice and celebrate. How sad I thought that Pa had not seen any of my children.

By the time George was three months old, we had another new king. Edward V11 had died on May 10th 1910 from a series of heart attacks which newspapers blamed on his self-indulgent lifestyle. He had been in the Navy and was quite a lad before he became King. Although he was married the public was well aware that he had many mistresses. But he had been a good King for us and we were sad. I thought about how we had all felt such a loss in Portsmouth when Queen Victoria died. Now we had lost her son too. About a week later he was buried at Windsor.

In the spring of the next year, we had a lovely visit from my very best friend Alice and her husband John Archer. John was from Leeds and worked as a clerk in the labour exchange. It was so good to see her and she was thrilled to see Harry and me so happy with all our little children. They made such a fuss of them. They hadn't got any children of their own yet. What a squash it was. We still had Molly boarding with us so we had to put the children in our bedroom so we could accommodate them. Alice had gone to live in Leeds with John and we discussed the differences up North from being in a seaside town in the South. We reminisced about those days, such a while ago, parading along the seafront in the sunshine so carefree and laughing. It was completely different here but we were each so happy with our husbands.

King George V was crowned at Westminster Abbey on 22nd June 1911. Once again after a year of mourning. Another excuse for a few drinks at the pub. Not for me at home with three young children and pregnant again. That would be four children under four.

It was hard work bringing up three youngsters. Eileen and Kathleen were full of mischief and ran rings around me while I was tending to George. How lovely to see them run along the hallway with arms open wide to greet their Dada as he arrived home from work. How proud Harry and I were as we took them to church on a Sunday dressed in their best clothes and polished bootees. I loved going to Mass on Sunday. Fr Rowan was such a lovely priest who welcomed everyone and knew everyone, often visiting us in our homes. Since being converted to Catholicism I found it to be my lifeline. After my housework was done, I often called with the children in the pram to visit Loreto Convent and Sister Andrea. She always welcomed us with a cup of tea and some cake for the children.

The washing and cleaning were never-ending. Every day the surfaces were covered in sooty greasy dust from the smoking chimneys. In the winter Manchester often suffered from the most awful damp smog which clung to the skin. A mixture of sooty smoke and fog which draped itself around the streets until it was impossible to see a thing in front of you. No wonder people kept themselves covered from neck to ankle. If I was out in it my face and neck were coated with a dirty film. It got up your nose, and in your mouth, as you breathed. Such a lot of people had coughs and chest infections which were probably caused by this. What a huge difference from the fresh sea mists in Southsea. I missed the lovely fresh seaside air.

Harry's sister Kitty had met and fallen in love with Denis O'Mahony, and at St Wilfred's Catholic Church in Hulme on Wednesday 2nd August 1911 Kitty was given away in marriage by Harry to Denis, who came from Fermoy in Ireland and was employed at the Manchester GPO. His friend Dan O'Donoghue was his best man. Mary and Lena, her sisters, and my Eileen and Kathleen were among the bridesmaids all dressed in pearl grey dresses. Kitty had a dress of champagne coloured silk and an old lace veil dressed with orange blossom. She looked beautiful. I was so proud of my little girls who managed to behave themselves well on the day. Another lively wedding reception put on by Mrs Curran and John was held at the house, this time at 217 Moss Lane East where Mrs Curran and family now lived. The whole wedding party was captured by a photographer in the back yard. I was three months pregnant at the time.

Kitty and Denis travelled to Ireland for their honeymoon but when they came back to Manchester Kitty became ill with pneumonia blaming the damp countryside of Ireland. To our horror and disbelief, Kitty passed away in October and after a Requiem Mass at English Martyrs Church she was buried with her brother Patrick in St Joseph's Cemetery, Moston. That winter was long and dark for us all especially Mrs Curran who took the loss of her daughter very badly. We just found it hard to believe she was gone. After all the excitement of the wedding plans, the joy of the wedding day, seeing the happiness and love of her and Denis. There were no Christmas celebrations or cards sent again for the Curran family, as was the Irish tradition. For us, it was hard work lifting the spirits for the sake of the little ones.

For all of us, the mood was lightened when Nora Patricia entered our world on 9th February 1912. This time a little fair-haired baby with deep brown eyes like her Dada. Less than 10 days after her birth, she was baptised at English Martyrs Church by Fr Rowan on 18th February. Mary Curran and John Collins, a friend of Harry, were her Godparents.

Then followed two years of happy family life. Eileen and Kathleen started school at Bishop Bilsborrow Infant School on Princess Road much to the consternation of their teacher, and the nuns from the convent, who had no idea who was who. I would walk them there and pick them up in the afternoon, pushing Nora in the pram with George sat on the end. Sometimes we would walk home through the park and let them have a run around for some fresh air before tea. I would try and keep some crumbs or a crust of bread for them to feed the ducks in the pond, who all came paddling as fast as they could for the offerings. Seeing them searching the bottom of the pond, upside down with tail feathers high in the air, always made the children laugh. Sometimes I sat and watched the bowling teams while the children ran around on the grass. It always took the energy out of them so they were ready to calm down for bedtime.

In 1913 we were shocked when one of the suffragettes, it said in the paper that it was Kitty Marion, put a bomb in our lovely new cactus house in the park and destroyed it. Such a mess. Glass was thrown everywhere and it was dangerous to play nearby in case the children cut themselves. People were outraged. What a pointless act of destruction.

Chapter Seven

How peaceful the house was once the children were asleep in bed. Such angelic little faces on their pillows. All the mischief of the day forgiven and forgotten. Harry and I would sit by the fire in the evening. He in his comfy armchair reading the paper, by the dim light of the gas mantle, and commenting on the news whilst I did my mending or knitting. The paper was the only way of getting any news unless you went to the picture house to watch films of the news. Occasionally we would get someone to babysit the children and Harry would take me to the Claremont Picture House or a variety show at Hulme Hippodrome, only a short walk away. We saw many popular silent films of the time, with the music from the organ emphasising the atmosphere.

Spring 1914 and here was I expecting another child. It seemed that as soon as I had weaned the baby, I would get pregnant again. This would make five and the eldest two only six years old. I had given up my life and family in Portsmouth for this and it was everything I had ever dreamed of. My whole life was devoted to Harry and our children. They were such a joy. Ours would be the best and happiest family it could be. I would do everything to make it so.

Harry told me there was a lot of talk among the men at work and in the public houses about the unrest between countries in Europe. On June 28th Archduke Franz Ferdinand and his wife were assassinated after an earlier attempt on their lives. Germany began to invade France and Belgium on the one side and Russia on the other. The Daily Mirror newspaper reported that Great Britain had requested that Germany should respect the neutrality of Belgium and that the German fleet should not bombard defenceless French towns. Germany had tried to bribe us with peace to desert our friends and duty, but

Harry said Britain had preferred the path of honour and rightly so. And so, on August 5th 1914 war was declared.

We were devastated. Harry was still a Regular Reservist after the Boer War thirteen years earlier. This meant that he was on call to his battalion whenever he was needed. Ready trained, ready for action. This scared us and we weren't sure what was going to happen.

Immediately a general mobilisation was proclaimed and notices were put in all the newspapers that all Regular Reservists were required to proceed at once to the place shown on their identity certificate without waiting for the formal notice. On his identity certificate was a cash order which the reservist was to present at the nearest post office where he would receive three shillings advance of pay and then take his certificate to the railway booking office where he would be given a ticket to travel to his place of joining. This was all to be done with the utmost urgency.

We were so shocked. We had never really thought Harry would be called up again. I was scared for him and for what it would be like. Three shillings in advance of his wages, how did they think that would help when I was losing my Harry? My poor Harry. The 36th Brigade Royal Field Artillery was taking back my Harry.

The day was spent packing his kit bag with essentials. I made sure there were paper and pencils so he could write to us. All the time tears kept brimming over, making it hard to focus. I would miss him so much, and what about the children missing him and all the what-ifs that kept going through my mind. We only had this day to discuss all the important things and all the small things.

Harry went to the post office and collected the three shillings advance for reservists and then went into work to collect the wages owed to him to date. Several other workmates were also there. Laughing and eager to serve, they went together to collect their travel documents, arranging which train they would go on the next day. He went to his mother's house and said his farewells to her and his sisters. They had done this before. I hadn't.

We spent the evening sitting close together talking about all the things I would have to take care of whilst he was away. It wouldn't be too long. This would be over in a couple of months when the Germans realised what they were up against. I promised to have some photographs taken to send to him. He would be back in time for our baby's birth.

The next morning, we drew the curtains to a sad damp drizzly Manchester day. We held each other and I took in the smell of him; his clothes, his hair, his skin, the feel of him; the broad dependable shoulders, the strong rough hands, the smooth shaved face, and the curl of his hair. The bristly moustache as we kissed. I wondered how long I would have to keep this memory until he came home.

I watched him walk down the street. My eyes could have burned holes in him, taking in every last memory of him. My heart had dropped into my stomach. The lump in my throat threatened to choke me. All my adrenaline had drained away. Arms limp at my sides. His best suit, cloth cap, kitbag over one shoulder, but already his demeanour had changed to the upright soldier in him. As he reached the corner he paused, turned, and lifted a hand to wave. With a smile, he blew a kiss and walked on. I climbed the three steps and shut the door behind me. Silence. Nothing. My footsteps echoed on the oilcloth as I walked along the hall. I sat with my hands in my lap, quietly dazed, wondering what I should do next. I must have been sitting there for quite a while when there was a knock on the door. I rushed to open it, somehow thinking he might be back and was surprised to see his mother who opened her arms to me and held me so tight as I sobbed into her shoulder.

Eleven days later, on 16th August 1914 Harry was drafted to The Western Front with the British Expeditionary Force and by the 23rd August into their first battle, the Battle of Mons.

We had no radios then and the way we got any news about our soldiers was from their letters, newspapers, or picture houses. News vendors in the town shouted news of the war's progress as they sold the papers on street corners. We all bought newspapers every day to find out what was happening. If we received letters, we shared our news. Mrs Curran was the backbone of the family and such a help to us. At Mass on Sundays, we prayed for our soldiers. I knelt and prayed the rosary every night after the children were in bed putting my faith in Our Lady. It was quiet and lonely by the fire in the evenings as I sat and tried to think what Harry might be doing. I wrote letters to him as often as I could trying to cheer him with news of the children and myself.

Posters started to appear on the side of trams encouraging young men to volunteer, not just to sit at home singing "Rule Britannia". In the theatres, the stars of the variety shows encouraged young men in the audience to come up on stage and sign up for the "King's Shilling." In the excitement of the night many men signed up without thinking about what they were doing and half regretted it when they got home. Pals were all encouraged to join up together to guarantee they would be in the same regiments. Volunteers were cheered as they marched from Manchester to the training camps in Heaton Park. Members of the suffragettes offered white feathers to men who weren't in uniform as a sign that they thought of them as cowards, such pressure was put on young men.

Mrs Curran took us all to the photography studio with the children in their best clothes to have a series of photographs taken so we could send them to Harry. The twins were six years old then and they missed their Dada but couldn't understand where he was. George was four and Nora was two. I was six months pregnant and looking rather large. Once again, my ankles were starting to swell and the summer heat didn't help. I tried to rest them and keep my feet up as much as I could. I couldn't afford to be told to bed rest when I had four children to look after. The routine of our days with the children helped to take my mind off what was happening in France and I devoured every word of the letters Harry sent to me. As an experienced soldier he seemed to be looked up to by the younger men who had volunteered. He had such a lovely nature that he would have been like a father to them and cajoled them with stories and jokes.

The papers published pictures of our soldiers smiling and the Pathe news at the picture houses showed them laughing and waving. It was made to look like they were having a good time. How else would they get more volunteers? The grim reality was, as we found out from soldiers' letters, that it was frightening even if you had served before. Being fired at by the Germans, shouted at by officers, scrabbling around in mud and rain, digging trenches and boarding them up. Army rations served in tins. Harry being a gunner was not on the front line. They backed up the infantrymen, firing over their heads at the enemy. The heavy gun carriages had to be pulled to new positions by the horses. From Mons to Le Cateau on 26th August, then to the Battle of Marne 6th to 12th September. From the beginning of October until 22nd November they were engaged in the Battle of Bassee and the Battle of Ypres. Marching from battle to battle in the muddy footsteps of the horses and carriages. Making camp on the frosty ground with duck cotton or canvas tents. Never getting warm and always wet and muddied when it rained.

Harry's letters arrived home giving us an idea of what it was really like. They were wet and cold. He sent a photo of himself and friends outside a conical tent which they slept in when not on duty, Summer and Winter, warm or cold, dry or wet, sun or snow. He also sent an official photograph of himself in full uniform taken in a studio. He asked if we could send some gloves and socks to replace the ones he had, which were always wet as the damp mud churned up by the horses and gun carriages soaked through their boots. Socks wore away from the damp with no wives there to darn the holes. He always included a loving word for his precious children. Concerned for me, he told me I should go to his mother if I needed any help. Always finishing his letters "love to all from your loving husband." They brought tears to my eyes. I was so worried about him and missed him terribly. I now started to knit gloves and socks whenever I took a rest. We prayed the rosary for our husbands, brothers and, sons. We went to church on Sundays and Fr Rowan offered prayers for them. Mother Andrea took to visiting us regularly telling me that prayers were being said by the nuns for Harry and his friends. She was such a breath of fresh air. Under all this strain life carried on, taking the girls to school, washing Mondays, ironing Tuesdays, walks to the park to see the ducks. Not feeding the ducks now as the food was getting scarce. Always we tried to keep a cheerful face. It was hard. It was routine that kept us going.

Chapter Eight

As winter approached and my time drew near, I wondered how I would manage. Mrs Curran told me that Delia would come and stay with me helping with the children and she would call daily. Such a relief. I was able to relax a bit and little Francis Noel was born in December. Harry was overjoyed at the arrival of another son but was unable to take leave to come home. Poor Harry how he must have yearned to see his new baby. No doubt he had a few pats on the back from his fellow soldiers.

Shortly before Christmas, Princess Mary had launched an appeal in the newspapers so she could send a Christmas gift to every soldier and sailor, fighting for our country. Harry wrote and told me how grateful they all were to receive these little brass boxes which were filled with an ounce of tobacco, a packet of cigarettes, a cigarette lighter, and a Christmas card and photograph from Princess Mary. Some of the boxes had sweets, chocolates, and lemon drops. There had been a ceasefire on Christmas Day and they had a makeshift church service after which they had all sat around singing Christmas Carols and talking of Christmas at home. The next day they were back to firing guns.

Christmas was very strange that year without Harry. We all did what we could to buy or make presents for the children wrapping small gifts and putting them in the stockings hung by the fireplace. Because it was easier for the children and myself having baby Francis, Mrs Curran came to my house and cooked Christmas Dinner for all the family. What a stalwart she was. Always rallying the family round.

I was soon up and about and had already had Francis Noel baptised. As soon as I could I had photos taken in the backyard of myself and Francis, Mrs Curran, and Nora so I could send them to Harry. Along with his letters Harry sent us beautifully embroidered postcards. They had been embroidered by the French ladies and sold to the soldiers to send home. In February a postcard arrived which read

"Dear Nora. Just a postcard to wish you many happy returns of your Birthday with fond love from Dada. I hope you will like the handkerchiefs."

He had sent her some delicate little handkerchiefs also beautifully embroidered. Another time, on one to me, he wrote

"Dear Nell, just a few lines hoping they find you well as they leave me here at present. I just found this and thought I would send it to you. No news, quite well here. Love to all from your loving Husband."

On a card to Nora, he wrote

"To Nora with love from her Dada in France."

All the children received these beautiful postcards at different times especially on their Birthdays or thereabouts. How kind he was to still be constantly thinking of us in his dire circumstances.

In all this turmoil I had not been in touch with family in Emsworth very much. Portsmouth must have been in upheaval with all the troops being transported to France and James had also volunteered as a driver in the army. I was surprised to receive a letter from Mama telling me that Uncle Henry and Aunt Kate had left Emsworth quite suddenly and returned to America. She said there had been a bit of trouble between them and Ann Belle and her husband. Things were always going wrong around Ann Belle.

In July 1915 I received a letter from Auntie Kate.

"Dear Niece Nellie,

*No doubt you were surprised to hear that we left home again.
Nevertheless, Uncle could not stand the way he was being
treated. No longer left our home and all to others. I think it is
a shame that not one of them tried to find out what it all meant.
They said they were not doing anything. Then why did they
not go to those parties that Uncle told them about and ask
them why their Uncle could not live in his house without being
molested. Well they will be the losers. Dear Nellie, how is
Harry. Has he been home to see you since he left? This cruel
war is causing lots of sorrow and trouble. I don't care if
Uncle never comes back to England again. We have had more
trouble in eighteen months than we had in our whole lives.
We were always so happy. I think something happened over
there and Annie was in it or she would have done something
to keep Uncle there. She sees us leave our home, two old
people, we don't want to be travelling about. We want our
home and the comforts of home life not roving about crossing
the ocean at our time of life. Had I known this I never would
have come to England in the first place when your Father was
living. However, it is too late to talk about it now. Well Dear
Nellie, I hope you are all enjoying good health as it leaves us
fairly well. Uncle has wasted away almost to a shadow. I
think it is horrible to think that they would do such a thing for
money. He intended to do good for them all. Well Nellie I
will close. Hope to hear from you soon. With love and kisses
to you and all the little ones. Remember us to Harry. We
remain your loving Aunt Kate and Uncle George Brockway.
Good Bye and God Bless you all."*

They had sailed from Liverpool on the "Saint Louis" to
New York and apologised that they had not had time to visit
beforehand. She sounded quite distraught. How awful. I

would love to have seen them before they went. Why was Ann Belle, and probably Mr Brock, causing trouble again? Drink and Mr Brock were bad for Ann Belle. Uncle Henry and Aunt Kate must have been desperate to travel now, when the Lusitania ship they had travelled here on, had lately been sunk in the ocean by the Germans. And it looked like they had cancelled a Will leaving all their possessions to the Brockway family.

December 1915 brought the joy of a home visit from Harry on leave. It was so comfortingly strange to have him in the house. He seemed different somehow. What had happened to my carefree Harry? He put on a brave face and was overjoyed to see us all but I would catch him in a quiet moment deep in thought and looking harrowed. He didn't talk about the battles they had been in but he struggled to sleep the whole night without waking disturbed. He sat with the children and told them stories that made them laugh. He delighted in being home for Francis' first birthday. Entertaining children leaves you no time to think of the more serious side of life.

We took pleasure in each other's company. He relaxed in the soothing hot waters of the tin bath in the warm glow of the coal fire as I soaped his back. A luxury he hadn't had for a long time. We cherished the quiet time together when the children were asleep. The firelight lighting his smiling face as we sat together in the backroom in those last evenings savouring every moment, every word, every touch.

But then, he was gone. He returned to his unit in France on Christmas Eve.

It might have been his visit or pressures from outside but on 12th December his brother John Joseph, who was a brewer's carter for a local brewery, had signed up and joined the Kings Shropshire Light Infantry. Poor Mrs Curran now had two sons in the army and one already killed in the mining accident.

The winter was dark and dismal, the days so short, the coal fire in the grate brought cosy comfort to our family as we sat together whilst I told them stories of heroes and seaside adventures. The fire warmed the room as I bathed them on Saturday evenings in the tin bath brought down from its hook on the wall. Hair washed and brushed, I tied rags into the girls' hair to form beautiful thick curls for the Sunday morning visit to church. The children asleep in bed I sat in the glow of the embers thinking how lucky we were here compared to the poor soldiers in the fields of France.

We welcomed the start of Spring, noticing the new leaf buds opening and casting a pale green hue on the trees in the park. I wondered if Spring was in the air in France and would any of the soldiers notice such small delights in their dreadful situations.

On the 9th March, a knock at the door delivered a letter from RH & RFA Record Office informing me that Harry had been killed on 1st March 1916.

Was that what it said? Had I read it right? My ears whooshed with the sudden rush of blood. My heart was in my mouth. My legs wobbled. No! No! He wasn't coming home. We wouldn't see him again. My darling Harry, father of my children, love of my life. No more.

A standard letter with spaces for the deceased soldier's details to be typed in. Was this all they thought of him. 22410 Gunner Harry Curran. So many being sacrificed it warranted a standard letter. Where was the compassion?

We were distraught. We didn't know how he had died. How badly had he suffered? Mary said we should be told and immediately wrote to his commanding officer who replied to her straight away. His letter written in pencil on squared paper bought in France.

"Dear Miss Curran,

In reply to your letter. The reason I have not written to your sister in law herself was that we have here gathered up a subscription in the event that he would take ill and have not quite finished it so as soon as that is finished, I will write to her. I can't tell you how much he is missed, as he was always so popular with the other men as you will tell by the subscriptions they are sending his wife. Also, I always found him such a hard working man & never grumbled whatever he was told to do. So, I can heartily sympathise with you and his poor wife. So, I will tell you all I know about how his death occurred. He was sleeping with three or four other men in the same billet and they heard a crash and at once lit a candle and found that the chimney had fallen down and some of the bricks had hit him. They at once went for the ambulance to send him to the hospital but on arriving there he was dead so did not suffer for very long. His friend was Bombardier Teager T 44083 of the same address and I have asked him to write you a full account so no doubt you will receive it shortly. Please explain both to his wife and mother the reason that I have not written before, also tell them how I sympathise with you all. Should there be anything that you want to know I shall be only too pleased to tell you.

A A Pelham. Capt RFA   UC 36 Brigade"

Tears trickled down my cheeks dripping onto the letter and soaking into the paper. Maybe they mixed with teardrops from his Captain as he wrote home to the families of his fallen men.

Total numbness. No thoughts. My Harry was gone. Thirty-six, that's all. Loving husband. Father. My Harry. Our Harry.

I had to share the grief with his family. The twinkling eyes, the loving arms around me. No more. Where was he?

Fr Rowan came to see us all as we sat around the living room, mother, sisters, and me. Ashen faced women. Solemn numbness. Silent tears slowly overflowed and trickled to drip from my chin. He prayed with us and arranged a memorial Mass for Harry at English Martyrs Church. No body. No funeral. No goodbye. Emptiness.

Mary put a notice in the newspaper for me with a photo of Harry.

"Manchester Veteran Killed. Mrs Curran of 104 George Street, Moss Side has been informed of the death in France of her husband, Gunner Michael Henry Curran, of the RFA. He served in the Boer War, and on the outbreak of war was recalled to the colours. In December last he was allowed home on leave but returned to the firing line on Christmas Eve. He was previously employed at the Salford Goods Station."

My world seemed to stop for a while and it was only with the support from the people around me that I pulled through. Fr Rowan and the nuns from Loreto were wonderful mentors to me and helped to get me through the bereavement. But now things were not so easy as we had no means of support until I was granted a meagre widow's pension. I would get a pension of 16s.3d and 6s. 8d for each of the children. In total, I would have to manage on £2.9s.7d a week. I could hardly keep five children and myself on such a small amount. I now had to take in washing, I couldn't go out cleaning as Francis was only fifteen months old and Nora four. Eileen, Kathleen and, George were all at school. To my shame, when I didn't have much work I had to go to the Parish for support. I hated that but for several years I was obliged to do this at times. Over the years to come, I did whatever work I could. I was determined to give my children a life as good as if they still had their Dada. Mine would be a happy family, a good respectable family, in a welcoming home. Even as we were trying to cope with such a small amount, the rationing of sugar and foodstuff came into force. It hardly affected us as we didn't have the money to buy it anyway.

Chapter Nine

Towards the end of the summer of 1918, Nora became very poorly with Rheumatic Fever and had to be admitted to hospital. Visiting her took up most of my time. I don't know what I would have done without the help of Harry's family who rallied round, looking after the other children and having a hot meal ready for me when I got home.

She was only six and at school at Bishop Bilsborrow Memorial School with her sisters and brother. We worried so much. She didn't seem to be improving, it seemed to be life or death. Mother Andrea sent me a lovely letter.

"Dear Mrs Curran, I am very sorry indeed to hear that dear Nora is not improving, but please God that the news you next hear will be better. The little ones have prayed especially to Our Lady of Lourdes for her recovery and you know what power their innocent prayers have with God. Meanwhile trust the Sacred Heart for He will spare your little one if He sees it is for the best."

She eventually recovered but it took quite some time for Nora to get back to her usual self. The illness had taken it out of her. She always was such a little slim thing. Quite to my surprise a lovely lady from our parish offered to take Nora out for rides in her pony and trap away from the built-up areas and down the country lanes past Whalley Range and around Alexandra Park Aerodrome to get some fresh air. I think it might have been suggested to her by Fr Rowan. He was so thoughtful. It was all open country and farmland from there to the River Mersey and the aerodrome had been constructed the year before on Hough End Fields.

Although we didn't have mills and factories in Moss Side, belching out dark plumes of smoke, we did have coal fires in every house which poured dark smoke into the atmosphere.

When there was no breeze or it was misty this just hovered around and caused smog, leaving behind dark smuts where it settled. It settled in the lungs and caused chronic coughing. Not many were spared of this. What a difference to the clean salty air of Portsmouth. I decided I would take Nora there as soon as I could to help her recover.

November arrived and as I was doing my housework there was an almighty din. What was all that banging in the street, lots of shouting, dustbin lids being banged together? A loud knocking at my door summoned me to open it to Mrs Watson from next door.

"It's over, It's over. Thank God it's over."

The Manchester Evening Newspaper had been brought out onto the streets of Manchester with the shouted news that the war was over. The shouting had now carried the news all the way from the city centre to Moss Side. We stood in the streets and hugged each other. On 11th November 1918 we were overjoyed to hear that a Peace Agreement had been signed and the War was over. Celebrations took place all over the country. Four years it had taken when we thought it would be over in six months. So many men lost or injured. So many families in mourning.

Our family was in emotional turmoil, Harry had been killed but thankfully his brother Jack would now return home safely. Mrs Curran had lost two sons but still had Jack. Children in school were given decorated "Peace Mugs". But shortly after, as the soldiers started to return, a deadly flu virus filtered in with them. It was rife among the troops and they took it back to their home countries. Oh, how we were blessed that our family managed to escape this deadly virus. We had had enough troubles already. So many people were lost, people we knew, people we didn't know.

After the war as I struggled to manage, I was helped by the nuns at Loreto who offered Nora a place at their preparatory school for a while. She was given a uniform gymslip to wear to school. She tried hard at her work. She tried to learn the violin and we all covered our ears when she brought it home to practise. Violins only sound good when played perfectly, definitely not when being practised around the house. George used to throw things at her to stop. I almost apologised to the neighbours.

George was lucky enough to be given a place at a boarding school in Dublin which was for the sons of army soldiers. My precious George left home and settled in school there and received a good education and learned to play the trumpet in the band. Perhaps Nora would have thrown things at him if he had had to practise at home. This education stood him in good stead and he was able to join the police force when he left school. I missed him so much but I knew it was the best opportunity for him. It left an empty space in our home, until school holidays when he joined us again.

Things were difficult moneywise with no wages coming in. I accepted all the help I could get for the sake of my children. When it came to winter, I made sure they all had warm clothes and shoes to wear. They were growing so fast. It was make do and mend, pass down and alter. Unravelling old woollies to knit socks and mittens. I would do without, myself so that they were well fed and well presented.

The twins were such little imps. One winters day the lake in Alexandra Park had frozen over and people were permitted to skate on it. My young ladies Eileen and Kathleen went off to the park to watch them and decided to join in but not having skates didn't stop them. Such a good time they had sliding about in their best shoes. I gave them a good telling off when they came home with soaking wet shoes but it didn't stop them going and doing the same again the next day. They thought I wouldn't notice if they sneaked in the back door but I heard the latch on the yard gate and was there waiting for their return.

As the children grew and explored their surroundings, they often walked to Alexandra Park Aerodrome where if they stood on top of the railway bridge, they had a good view of the planes which left each morning for Croydon. They always made a special day out there when there was a flying display by Lancashire Aero Club. It was still quite a dangerous way to travel though and the ticket agent on receiving a telegram from Croydon that they had landed safely would dispatch a messenger boy to the travellers' homes with the news

I kept in touch all the time with Mama, writing letters frequently to tell her all the things the children were getting up to and how they were growing into such a lovely family. I got long loving letters back from her that healed any rift there had been about my wedding. It would have been so nice if she had lived nearer and been able to enjoy my children. Three years after the end of the war Mama was very poorly and I had a letter from solicitors asking permission to sell property from Pa's estate by auction for a lower price as it still hadn't sold. Ann Belle and her husband were living in it and weren't paying their rent and the solicitor was giving them notice to quit. I think Ann Belle and her husband had a lot of problems all to do with drinking and living the good life. She should have been helping Mama, not causing her more distress. Always Ann Belle causing trouble. We all said Mr Brock was a really bad influence on her but then she always was a bit wayward and liked a drink. I gave my permission and hoped I would be able to go and see Mama as soon as possible but our situation didn't allow me. I had only been to Emsworth once since the war finished and taken Nora after she had been so poorly, hoping the sea air would strengthen her.

Mama was seventy-three when she passed away on 26th March 1922. This time I visited for her funeral. We buried her in plot 104 with Pa in the Warblington Cemetery. It was not a good time to be with family and things were difficult. We can't choose our families and we can't always see eye to eye. I didn't stay long, I needed to get back for the children. Such a lot of illnesses and deaths.

Father Rowan, English Martyrs' Parish, the Loreto nuns, and my faith were such a strength for me to fall back on each time I slumped. They also encouraged Nora to join the Brownies at the church. She stayed in the Brownies until she left school having worked her way up to Brown Owl looking after the younger ones.

There were lots of shortages after the war and good nourishing food was hard to come by to feed a large family. Clothes needed replacing as the children grew. I patched and altered what I could with the help of Harry's sisters and Mother. With the help and encouragement of Mrs Curran who was so strong, we kept our dignity and kept up appearances.

Once as children sometimes do, Nora asked her Nana for a penny only to be told off severely. "Don't ever let me hear you begging." Her attitude was understandable having the background she did, coming from Ireland when there had been famine and beggars had wandered the streets. But Nora never forgot that. We tried not to show how we struggled. This in itself convinced us that we were doing alright. We were still a happy loving family and we all helped where we could. The girls would sometimes go and donkey stone the steps of the houses down the road to earn a penny or two which they always brought home to me first. We sometimes took in a lodger or two to help make ends meet. To do this we all had to squash up and make one of the bedrooms available. We once took in a young couple and their baby. The baby was very poorly and during the night he passed away. Kathleen told me the next morning that she knew he had died because she had seen a bright light in her bedroom going up to the sky. It makes you think.

1 Sultan Road, Emsworth   6 Allens Road, Southsea

Southsea Beach

Ellen Keily/Curran

John Curran

Michael Henry Curran

Bridget Curran

Mary
Curran

Helena
Curran

Kathleen
Curran

Marriage of Ellen Elizabeth Brockway and Michael Henry Curran

Curran Children   Michael Henry Curran

Alexandra Park, Moss Side

104 Criccieth Street (late George Street) Moss Side
Curran Family Home, Second Bay Window.

Chapter Ten

I was so sad to receive a letter from Auntie Kate in America telling me that Uncle Henry, who had been living in a home for the feeble-minded had died on 28th March 1926. He was seventy-six. He was buried in Marticville, Lancaster County, Pennsylvania. It had been eleven years since they had gone back to America so suddenly. I wondered if the trouble he had had here, had put him on a downward spiral only to end up with dementia. Poor Auntie Kate.

A formal letter came from a solicitor in America telling us that Uncle Henry had died without leaving a will and therefore James, Ann Belle, and myself would be entitled to inherit a share of the estate as children of his late brother James.

Sadness, numbness, guilty joy. How awful to think like that, but we would be getting some money. I, ashamedly, wondered how much it would be and dreamed that it might be enough to not worry about where the next meal was coming from. Poor Auntie Kate, I am sure she would not be happy that Ann Belle was going to inherit some of his money after all the worry she had caused him.

The solicitor was coming to England on the S.S.Minnetonka, which would take almost eight days, and would like to meet us all in Emsworth on Sunday 25th July, to establish our identities. I would have to travel down by train and stay over until Monday. I could have left Nora and Frank with Eileen and Kathleen who were eighteen then, but Nora wanted to come with me hoping to see her cousins.

The solicitor was staying at the Crown Hotel on High Street and that was where we would be meeting him. That hotel was a bit too expensive for me so we booked in at the Railway Hotel on the corner of Sultan Street where I used to live.

Sunday afternoon and Nora and I, having already had a stroll along Sultan Street for old times' sake, headed off to the Crown a good ten minutes' walk away. We met up with Ann Belle and James and the solicitor who was a well dressed young American with a New York accent when he spoke. He hoped that having confirmed our identities, things might be completed by January the next year. When we asked, he couldn't tell us how much we would get as there was all the paperwork to do and property to be sold, including the house they still owned, Northville, in Westbourne Avenue Emsworth. I felt a bit deflated about having to wait all that time, as I was struggling moneywise and out of desperation asked might we be able to get any money in advance. Oh no, things didn't work like that. It was against the law.

Making the most of our short visit, Nora and I walked down through the town until we came to the Solent Way, a quiet coastal path that led us to Warblington Cemetery surrounded by fields and almost in the shadow of Warblington Castle. The tide was in as we walked in the late afternoon, listening to the sound of the waves lapping on the shore next to the path. Through a shaded, wooded area the path opened out into farmland with the cemetery ahead. Paying our respects, we put flowers on the grave of Mama and Pa. So many memories flooded back and it was good to have Nora with me to talk to.

Travelling back on Monday morning, we didn't know how much we would receive or when we would receive it. So, life carried on as before but always hoping it would come soon. January 1927 came and went and still, we heard nothing. It wasn't until February 1928 that I received a letter. We each, Ann Belle, James, and I, received £5,699.7s.1d. Our lives would now really change for the better with that amount.

Thank you, Uncle Henry and Auntie Kate. Thank you, thank you, thank you.

1928. Eileen and Kathleen were twenty, George eighteen, Nora sixteen, Frank fourteen. Our lives were changing. Eileen and Kathleen had been working in shops since they were fourteen, George had joined the police force. Nora had been a pupil at St Joseph's Technical Convent School in Victoria Park which was run by the Little Sisters of the Poor. She stayed on at school until she was sixteen and received her leaver's certificate in July 1928 and a reference which she was so proud of. Sister Agnes had written;

"Nora Curran has spent five years at this school and has always given the utmost satisfaction. She is a very smart intelligent girl and has just taken the School Certificate Examination, at which we trust she has been successful. Nora is thoroughly honourable and reliable and most polite and obliging. She should give every satisfaction to any employer"

She went to work in the Manchester Transport Office as a clerk. Francis or Frank as we called him now left school and went to work for a butcher learning the trade.

By now things had changed so much from when I was a young girl. The suffragette movement and the fact that women had been doing men's jobs during the war had given girls and women a new sense of who they were and what they wanted to do. During this year we were granted the same rights as men to vote in the elections when we reached twenty-one. It was a huge victory for all the hard work and devotion of the suffragettes. There were also, since the war, more eligible women than men. Styles had changed and now the tight waisted corsets disappeared and dresses became straight with a band around the hips. Much to my horror skirts were now worn just below the knee. My ankles were so thick I stayed in my long skirts. Not only this but my girls also cut off their lovely long hair into a "bob" which was short into the nape of the neck like a boy's. This short hair allowed them to wear a pull-on hat like a bonnet with no straps, called a cloche. They went dancing in the new dance halls doing the "Charleston" and kicking up their legs. They had such fun with all this freedom and I found myself a bit envious of that freedom. My upbringing had been so straight-laced and proper.

With all my family out and about socialising it was hard to keep abreast of who their friends were, so I took the easy, but hard work way out. I held open-house every Friday night for them to bring their friends home. I would cook a big hotpot for everyone and they would sing around the piano. There was always someone who could play. That way I could meet their friends informally and get to know what they were like and also enjoy myself. I never had this at home myself but had learned from the Curran family's hospitality.

Eileen and Kathleen once again were rascals with their boyfriends. When Eileen didn't want to meet her current boyfriend anymore, she would send Kathleen in her place to tell him the bad news. They had such fun confusing people because it was difficult, even for me, to tell them apart. I can't begin to think about what else they got up to. Being identical must be so much fun sometimes.

Nora missed having a sister who was close in age. She joined the Whalley Range Tennis Club just near English Martyrs Church and travelled to other clubs playing matches. She met lots of friends there and also through groups visiting from other Catholic Parishes. She joined a hiking group and went on walking holidays with the Christian Holiday Fellowship, all around the country; the Lake District, Scotland, Ireland, and Wales.

A nearer day out was taken by lots of people from Moss Side. On a bank holiday, we would all take the trolley bus to Northenden where there was a country fair on the banks of the River Mersey. There were side stalls, boxing booths, country sports, and boat rides on the river. People came from as far as Blackpool on a charabanc for a day out.

Northenden was a small village with a church, St Wilfrid's, and several public houses. It was on the other side of the river into the Cheshire countryside and near Wythenshawe Hall and Park. By the 1930s Manchester had bought Wythenshawe and Northenden from Cheshire creating a new county boundary and started to build houses for its expanding population away from the smoke and grime.

Nothing changed in our rented house. The landlord never did anything to update our situation. We still had no electricity in the house. He never did any repairs or maintenance.

I had a real scare one day when I was cleaning the windows. The windows in our house were sash windows, which moved up and down on a rope pulley on each side of the frame. To clean outside I had to lean out backwards and reach up to the top window pane. As I was doing this, the old frayed pulley rope snapped and the whole frame slid down onto me, trapping me. I just could not get enough power in my arms to raise it. I didn't know what to do. The children were all out at work. I thought I'd still be there when they got home from work in the evening. I started to shout for help but couldn't see anyone as I was facing the window. I felt so stupid. After what seemed an eternity, a neighbour several doors away came along the back entry looking where the shouting was coming from. He saw my distress and came through the backyard gate. Fortunately, we hardly ever locked the back door so he was able to come in and rescue me by easily lifting the window panel from inside. Luckily, I wasn't hurt. Just my pride at being in such a vulnerable position. It was such a funny story for everyone else and was told and retold, to anyone who listened, for years to come.

This wasn't the only time I had an accident. The coal for our fire was dropped from a sack, through a covered hole next to the front doorstep into the cellar. It arrived in a big heap at the bottom of the cellar steps, so whenever I needed coal, I had to take a bucket down the steps and fill it. As we had no electricity, it was usually dark and gloomy down there so I had to take a candle to light my way. Carrying a bucket and a candle left me with no hands to steady myself as I went down the steps. One day as I was doing this, I tumbled down the steps and landed at the bottom. Having put out an arm to save myself, I, unfortunately, realised that the arm that saved the rest of me was so painful that I felt sick. I am not sure how long I sat there wondering what to do and trying to regain my senses. My arm hurt so much. Once again, I was home alone in the house. All the family was out at work. Why was no one ever in when I needed them. My candle had blown out and I sat there in the dark breathing in coal dust and feeling sorry for myself. Eventually, I decided there was only one person who could help and that was me. I cradled my poor arm and carefully stood up. I felt quite wobbly and had to sit down again until I felt better.

After some time, I managed to climb the cellar steps back into the house. By now the fire had gone out and I hadn't brought any coal up. I looked at the clock. It would be about an hour before one of the children came home from work. I decided to just wait for them. No tea on the table tonight. Eileen and Kathleen were first home and immediately took charge. Kathleen got a taxi cab to pick us up and take us to the hospital. Eileen stayed home and prepared the evening meal. It was such a relief to be looked after when I was feeling so bad. The hospital doctor said I had broken a bone in my arm and set it in plaster. He suggested no heavy duties for me for a week or two until it felt as if it was getting better. I don't think he knew how resilient I was. I won't say I didn't enjoy being looked after by the girls for a while though.

As time went on, they all met their partners to be. Eileen met and married Sidney Miles, a bricklayer, and went to live in Coney Grove in Baguley. This was in the new estate that Manchester Council had built on land from Cheshire. They were two-storey houses with a black leaded oven in the kitchen, back to back with the fire grate in the living room. They also had a bathroom and an inside toilet. These were downstairs behind the kitchen. What luxury, not having to traipse to the end of the backyard in the cold, or to fill and empty a tin bath every week. They all had gardens back and front, not like our yards. A chance to grow flowers and vegetables.

Kathleen met and married Wilfred, a butcher, the son of my friend Mrs Frost, and lived in Garswood Road across Princess Road past Alexandra Park. These too were more modern houses than the one we lived in, also belonging to Manchester Council. The bonus of them being in council houses was that, unlike my landlord, the council would do all the repairs.

George met and married Norah Kennerley and they lived in a police station house in Stoke on Trent. That meant I didn't see him as often as I would like but I had grown used to it and always made the most of it when they could get to Manchester.

Frank met and married Kathleen Ryan. They lived just near Platt Fields, a bus ride away until they bought a butcher's shop on Withington Road and moved into the flat above. He always brought our weekly supply of meat from his shop.

Nora had been courting with a gentleman for a few years but had broken it off. She was the only one left at home. She was working in the offices for Manchester Transport. How relaxing and comforting to see the children happy and settled but a bit of me was pleased I still had one of them living with me. I had worked so hard through good times and troubled times to raise them as respectable happy loving people and I now believed I had. No family is perfect but most of the time we were happy and I was proud of them.

Chapter Eleven

I now had my own social life and enjoyed watching and playing bowls for the Ladies Team in Alexandra Park. I was eventually elected as one of the vice presidents. I had a good friend in Mrs Frost who played bowls and was also a widow. We would meet up and go to the pictures or, now I could afford it, we sometimes went to the seaside on the train for a day or on a holiday. Blackpool or Rhyl but always to the seaside. How I loved the fresh salty air and a cone of cockles or winkles from the kiosks along the beach. We would hire deckchairs and sit on the promenade watching the families playing on the beach or the rush of waves on the incoming tide.

Just like the old days but sadly not with my Harry.

My financial status now was good. Since receiving the inheritance from Uncle Henry, I had been sensible with the money. I had enough money that I could have easily bought a house for us but nothing was going to get me out of the home that Harry and I had put together. I had given a good amount to each of the children to help them get a start in their lives. In 1935, I bought and paid for a family burial plot in Southern Cemetery. I bought plot no. 574 in Section D which was in the new Roman Catholic part. It cost me £4.19s.0d. Several other family members and friends all bought their plots around there at the same time. The area was new and open and bright with young trees near the Catholic Chapel. Not dark and dismal like St Joseph's Cemetery in Moston. With the essentials taken care of, I could now take the chance to enjoy myself a little.

Around 1935 a knock on the door had me opening it to a policeman in uniform. My heart leapt into my mouth wondering what he was going to say. Always the worse things run through your mind. He stepped inside and told me to sit down. He asked was I related to Nora Curran. Oh God no! I mean yes! He told me that Nora had been in an accident when the bus she was travelling on had crashed. She was badly injured and had been taken straight to the hospital. Such a kind policeman, he took me in the police car straight to the hospital.

Nora never remembered anything about the accident, as she had been knocked unconscious and only came around in the hospital. I sat by her bed holding her hand. She was so pale. It was a very worrying time and took her a long time to recuperate. Always it seemed to be Nora. Perhaps I worried about her more because she had been so ill as a little one. Her bedside was overflowing with get well cards and flowers from all her friends at work and the tennis club. Quite a show of how popular she was.

With my upbringing in a seafaring port, it had always been a dream of mine to go on a cruise, and now, hoping it would help her to convalesce, I asked Nora if she would like to go with me. She was thrilled to be able to go abroad and we booked a trip to Madeira. This would help her to build up her strength. I knew how good sea air could be. But most of all, this was my dream being fulfilled too.

We booked the cruise on the T.S.S Voltaire (Turbine Steam Ship) of the Lamport and Holt Line for the 1st to 14th August 1936. I thought at that time of year it would be fairly calm and agreeably warm as we were sailing on a round trip from Southampton to Madeira. The most I had ever done before now was the ferry from Portsmouth to the Isle of Wight.

As the time drew near, we busied ourselves with buying all the right outfits for cruising. We needed lots of advice on this. Nora's friends, who were very fashion-conscious and well dressed, were so excited for her and they spent many days visiting Pauldens and Lewis's studying the latest fashions. I knew how people with class behaved and I hoped we would be able to hold our own.

July came to an end and we had forwarded a trunk full of clothing to Southampton to be stowed in our cabin, all carefully packed with tissue paper to avoid creases. We only needed to take a small suitcase each as we boarded the train from Manchester to Southampton. We were so excited. The booking agent had shown us a brochure of the liner with some wonderful pictures.

Five hours later, arriving at the docks it was all hustle and bustle with porters taking on suitcases, trunks, and crates of supplies for the journey. Noisy with the sharp cries of the seagulls as they swooped and soared above the ship. It was busy with papers being checked. Goodbyes were being said with hugs and kisses. We boarded by the gangplank and were welcomed aboard. Our small cases were taken from us by a bellboy who led us to our cabin, with our hands full of information leaflets about the cruise; the entertainment, dining times, sporting competitions, and a list of passengers.

As it became time for the liner to leave port we hurried to the top deck. What a spectacle. We edged and nudged our way to the side rails for a good view of the dock as we left. The shore was packed with waving hands and white handkerchiefs, all faces turned upwards to the decks. The ship's siren sounded and a band on board began to play as we slowly moved away. My heart fluttered with excitement and I held Nora's hand. I closed my eyes and took in the salty breeze that reminded me of my childhood. How fresh and bracing. We were certainly going to enjoy this.

After trying to find our way around the ship we were totally in awe of the elegance. Everything was so luxurious and rich.

The brass banisters shone to perfection in the glow of the electric lights of the chandeliers and our feet sank with the deep comfort of silent footsteps into the thick pile of the carpets as we moved around the ship. The staff were dressed in black uniforms with spotless white shirts. The entertainment staff wore white trousers and blue blazers with a trim around the lapels. All had shiny brass buttons. All had name badges. All had such welcoming smiles. We returned to the cabin and dressed for dinner. There were two sittings 6.45 pm or 8 pm. We chose the earlier time as we had been travelling all day and were very hungry.

All dolled up in our finery, we felt very grand. We didn't have opportunities like this to dress up at home. Looking around we smiled and agreed that the new dresses we had chosen were indeed very fashionable and just the correct clothes for this sort of company.

Waiters in impeccable suits showed us to a table which already had some people seated. I felt a little nervous about meeting new people but Nora took over immediately and introduced us. As they introduced themselves to us, we tried hard to remember their names because if we met up with them again it would seem rude if we didn't. The best way, we decided, would be to tick them off on our passenger list in the cabin when we went back. Several of the people on our table were single and Nora soon made new friendships.

Trying to look as though we lived like this all the time, we looked at the menu. We were offered soup, fillet of sole, or asparagus for starters. The main courses were fore and hindquarters of lamb, braised turkey, civet of hare, or gammon all served with fresh vegetables, rice or potatoes, or salmon salad. Desserts were exquisite, followed by cheese and biscuits and tea or coffee. Oh, my goodness how would we cope with all this richness and choice for two whole weeks? Bottles of wine were poured freely by the waiters, with dinner, and an orchestra played dance tunes and popular numbers at one end of the dining room. Such luxury I didn't know existed. After our very plain recipes and thriftiness at home, we were in heaven.

Our first day was at sea and the entertainment team encouraged and cajoled us into joining in the tournaments. We put our names down for the Whist Drive but didn't win even a consolation prize. Nora entered the Deck Tennis Ladies Singles, Deck Quoits Mixed Doubles and, Padder Tennis Mixed Doubles. These were to be played on the several days we were at sea. When it came to Padder Tennis, Nora was partnered by Mr Cowan who proved to be quite proficient and they came runners up. They all had such fun and the young people became very friendly. I was happy for Nora to socialise and to leave me sitting in a deckchair watching the sea go by feeding my memories of times by the sea with Harry. Oh, happy days.

We called into the port of Lisbon and having decided we would do some site seeing, we went ashore and joined our guide. We walked around the cobbled streets admiring the grand palaces and squares with their fountains and statues. The brilliance of the white and pastel shades of the houses amazed us after the smoke dirtied walls of Manchester. White houses and buildings, red-tiled roofs, turquoise sea. Beautiful. Just the sight of these fresh colours in the sunshine lifted our hearts. Everyone had plenty to discuss at dinner that night.

When we arrived at Funchal, we decided to take the rack railway up to the top where there was a small chapel. Walking around there we had marvellous views down over the town and the harbour where our ship looked so small. I don't know why I let them talk me into it but I joined the young ones for the trip down on the famous running sledges. We sat two in a sledge with two men in local costume, white suits and straw boaters, one either side, running alongside, jumping on and guiding the sledge over the polished cobbles at such a speed it took my breath away. Whizzing around corners at breakneck speed. Goodness knows how they did it. Much to my relief, although I did like the excitement, we were soon at the bottom and exploring the beautiful gardens, with their exotic flowers, and the tea rooms.

How time flew on that cruise. I hardly saw Nora who was enjoying her newly made friendships so much. It was good to see how well she was looking with a slight golden glow to her skin. Me, I wasn't unsociable and I did enjoy my time chatting with several ladies I had met but I spent a lot of time soaking up the atmosphere, sitting in my deckchair. I thought of Pa and the years he spent at sea. His days would have mostly been below deck. First as a stoker then as a cook, he would have been in the galleys all day. But he would have had a chance to take in the freedom and majesty of the seas and the quaint foreign ports where they docked. He would have been used to the fast-talking, foreign languages and, the local customs and dresses. Still, he would have been coming back to Portsmouth where it was light and airy, not to a place like Manchester.

I wish I had given the other children this opportunity but they were already settling into married life with their partners. I bought lots of small souvenirs for them all, to give them a flavour of our travels. The last few days were spent at sea on our journey back past Portugal and France and into Southampton. Soaking up the sun, presenting prizes, exchanging addresses with new people who we would probably never see again. Making the most of the wonderful choice of food and luxurious surroundings.

All packed up and ready to disembark, we stood at the rails and watched as we came into the harbour. Seafaring travellers must have done this so many times. Pa certainly had, returning to Portsmouth Harbour eager to be home with Mama and his children. Harry and other soldiers, returning from the horrors of war and looking forward to some semblance of peace and security. It seemed like such a long time since we stood here watching the land disappear. Now we were gliding towards it and the crowds waiting to greet us, porters waiting to take luggage. As we drew closer and the figures grew, a mass of hands waved urgently in recognition of their loved ones. Not for us. All our family was at home in Manchester.

On the train back we sat quietly, each lost in our own thoughts, as the movement of the train gently rocked us. The excitement of the last fortnight had exhausted us and we hadn't realised just how much till now. The compartment door slid back and a guard let us know that the refreshment carriage was now open for lunch. Taking our handbags, we walked carefully along the corridor and found ourselves a dining table. We now had such expensive food tastes after being spoiled for two weeks. Maybe we should just have a light lunch and a glass of wine before getting back to my normal glass of stout. What tales we had to tell everyone when we got back. I had fulfilled my dreams and I think I gave Nora an appetite for foreign travel. Such a sociable person, she probably couldn't wait to get back to her established group of friends and their open-topped cars.

Nothing like my youth. Nowadays girls and ladies knew exactly what they wanted from life and it wasn't always a husband. They wanted independence, careers, and respect as equals. The social changes had been enormous and I wasn't keeping up very well even though I tried. But no bobbed haircuts for me or knee-length skirts. Although my hemline had risen enough to show my shoes and ankles, I was certainly not going to the dance halls doing the Charleston or ballroom dancing to the big bands.

There were so many motor cars now. Everything was moving so much faster with engines rather than horses. Although there were some passenger aircraft, most travels were still done by car, bus, charabanc, or train.

Probably the biggest change was having a wireless radio in our homes. As we still had no electricity in our house, it was run on a battery which had to be charged up at the shops. Just think of all that news and entertainment without leaving the house. After I had done my housework, if I wasn't going out, I loved to sit and listen to some music. It was such welcomed company for me while Nora was out. I could snuggle down in my cosy chair by the fire and spend my evening listening to a musical recital or laughing at comedy shows.

How quiet the house was when Nora was out. After the hustle and bustle of five children running around the place, five young people, and all their friends on a Friday night, the silence was deafening. I could almost hear my big aspidistra plant growing in its pot.

Twenty years now since I lost Harry. Only his memories to keep me company in the glow of the fire. Remember Harry, sitting here the night before you left. Such a long time ago but I can still feel your arm around me, still smell the scent of you. I close my eyes and let my mind wander.

Chapter Twelve

Nora had certainly acquired an interest in travel now and in 1937 she arranged to travel with friends to Switzerland by train. She was able to book the holiday through Workers Travel Association Ltd. WTA Ltd was also associated with the Holiday Fellowship group which promoted walking holidays and house parties for workers. Nora and her friends had been on a lot of Holiday Fellowship walking holidays in Scotland, Ireland, and the Lake District. This time they were going to venture further.

They travelled to London and wearing their WTA badges were met on the platform of Cannon Street railway station by a travel representative and shown to their seats. They went by Channel Ferry and picked up their train in Ostend. The holiday included all meals, but only from the second day, so they had to take food for their evening meal on the train. On the way back, the leaflet encouraged them to buy from the leader a voucher for a meal box on the Ostend steamer. It would cost 2s.6d for three sandwiches, one egg, one packet of biscuits, one slice of cheese, and fruit. The information which was given to them certainly satisfied me that it was well organised. Goodness, I shouldn't have been worrying about her she was twenty-five. They had a wonderful holiday around Lake Lucerne walking, sightseeing and socialising. I was delighted when Nora brought back fine-looking gold watches for us both. Beautiful Swiss watches and very expensive.

That was in 1937. At that time, it didn't occur to us that the unrest was once again starting in Europe. Germany had Adolf Hitler as their leader and he was promising the German people he would make their country great again.

Even though most of my children were married now, we still all got together whenever we could. It was usually on a Wednesday afternoon when the shops were closed for the half-day or on a Sunday. Eileen and Kathleen worked in shops as did Frank who was now fully qualified as a butcher. The girls called round as often as possible. For Eileen, it was about six miles on a bus to come from Royal Oak in Wythenshawe. I loved to make them all welcome for a meal when they visited with their spouses. Frank visited every week to bring me my meat order. It certainly was a bonus having a butcher for a son. They were all doing so well for themselves. George and Norah, I didn't see so often as they were living in Stoke. Sometimes, if Stoke Football Club was playing Manchester City or Manchester United, he would come to the match and stay overnight. It was lovely to have a whole evening with him.

Then over the next few years, I became Grandma to several babies as they all started their families. George had Maureen, Michael, and Eileen. Frank had Christine. Eileen had Patricia, and Kathleen had Fred. Nora was lagging well behind them. She wasn't even married yet. She loved it when the grandchildren visited and she made such a fuss of them. A trip to Alexandra Park was always a must for a bit of fun. The grandchildren loved to be together and made their own fun. I often wondered what it would have been like if we still had Harry. How he would have loved this large happy family. So close and happy together. How I wished I could have shared these times with him. I felt he was watching over us from above and sometimes in a special moment I would feel his warmth around me which would make me smile.

Nora had met Herbert Briggs at the Tennis Club and through Church socials. He was well known to her as part of their social circle but until now, he had not been someone special to her. Now they started going out together as a couple. Bert lived at home, 3 Beech Grove, Longsight, with his Father, a retired tailor, and his unmarried sister Marie. Marie also had charge and cared for Margaret, the daughter of their sister Carrie, who had died from TB when Margaret was young. Margaret was more like a younger sister to Bert.

Bert had started his working life as a trainee clerk to a solicitor. When jobs had been very hard to come by in the depression, gentlemen much more educated than himself, were writing to his employer begging to be taken on. It had worried him to think he might lose his job to another person. But then his solicitor had died and left him without a job anyway. He now worked as a shipping clerk in Manchester. Although he was seven years older than Nora, he passed the family test and was welcomed by our family.

In those days, unless they had already made arrangements to meet, everyone communicated by post. It was quite usual to post a letter by teatime and for it to be received the next morning. How many sentiments had been committed to paper and stowed away in treasure boxes by the receiver? Bert and Nora kept company for a few years and as the breadwinner for his family, I suppose it was hard for him to commit to getting married. The answer came with the troubles in Europe.

In Germany, Adolf Hitler's influence increased, and in 1939, with his huge following that believed he would make Germany powerful again, he overstepped his mark. On September 1st he invaded Poland. We listened with immense interest and horror for every news broadcast. England joined with France and demanded that the Germans withdraw from Poland. Germany refused and it became clear that they could only be stopped by force.

At church that Sunday we prayed for peace in Europe and memories of the last war came back to me. Such evil for hardly any reason. What a terrible waste of life. I sat with Nora after Mass listening to the wireless for any news.

At 11.15 am 3rd September 1939 prime minister Neville Chamberlain announced that war had been declared on Germany. It didn't sink in really. This had happened before and Harry had immediately had to leave us. This time our family had no reserve soldiers but we did have young men who would have to join up. I was not strong. Mrs Curran had been strong and held the families together when her sons had gone to war. I didn't feel I was able to step into her shoes. I desperately hoped this would not go further. I needed time to come to terms with the situation. Mrs Curran was now living with her daughter and I decided I needed some advice from this resilient woman. I would go on Monday after Nora had gone to work.

Nobody talked about anything but this horror which was happening to us again. We wondered if this war would be like the last one. The fighting was in Poland. Hitler was not heading our way. It might be a bit more advanced than the trenches as we now had different and better weapons; tanks, planes, and advanced guns. Who knew? No doubt they would still want all our men. For the first few months, all the fighting seemed to be in Scandinavia but in May 1940 Hitler invaded Belgium, France, Luxembourg, and the Netherlands. Our prime minister Neville Chamberlain resigned. He just hadn't been able to talk the Germans into peace as he thought he might. Winston Churchill became our new prime minister. I think he had a much more aggressive nature than Chamberlain.

Basic foodstuffs began to be rationed in that January and meat in May. We thought we would be alright with that but Frank was soon called up to join the army, so no extra meat from our butcher now. Poor Frank was only twenty-five and he was sent with his battalion to North Africa. Once again, I was praying the rosary. Please let me keep my son. Don't let me lose him as I lost Harry. George was not called up as he was a policeman.

As in the first war, women were called to do the jobs that men had left vacant when they joined up. Munition workers, headteachers, bus drivers, and conductors. Women were called to join the Women's Land Army, working on the farms where farm labourers had joined the forces. Women who might have worked in drapery and lingerie shops were now directed to the factories, without choice, to make munitions, bombs, and guns, on the machines left behind by men. Nora was lucky in that she worked in an office and had been directed to work in the Manchester Gas and Water Company in the centre of Manchester. They took over the control of all the small utility companies to make sure supplies were evenly shared and correctly used. Another office job and close to home. Thank goodness for that. I would still have her here with me.

Chapter Thirteen

We didn't know what this war would be like. Bombs had been dropped in the Spanish Civil War and by the Italians when they invaded Ethiopia. So, we were warned, on the wireless and in the newspapers, that we would need to shelter from the bombs when they came. We had all been issued with gas masks, great cumbersome leather things, to protect us if a gas bomb was dropped. Gas had played a big part in the last war. We had to carry these masks with us all the time. Children were given Mickey Mouse masks to encourage them to use them. If there was a gas attack, we were told, the wardens would spin their rattles in the streets for us to hear and shout "Gas, Gas." But as nothing was happening here a lot of people just ignored the advice thinking it wouldn't happen to us.

Children from all big towns were evacuated to the countryside away from the threat of bombings. From some of our local schools, children were sent to Blackpool. At the cinema, newsreels showed queues of children at Victoria Station, all with small suitcases or clothes in paper parcels, all with their gas masks strapped across their shoulders. They waved happily to their parents as they left. Some of them thought they were just going for a day out. I, at first, thought they were going on their own but it appeared that teachers were going with them to help get them safely placed. They were initially sent to the safety of the country at the first onset of war and fostered by farming and country village families

As nothing happened in the towns for the first few months many families, dearly missing them, brought their children home again. They had attended the village schools and mixed with the country children. There were lots of differences between town and country children which in itself caused conflict. Many had found loving foster parents but as some of the children returned home, we heard that they had been taken in only to help with the work on a farm or market garden whilst the men were away. I was so glad my children had all grown. Imagine if the same had happened during the Great War, all my little ones would have had to go away. I couldn't have lived with that. I couldn't have let them go. My small grandchildren were living in areas that didn't seem to be threatened as there were no local industries. There was much confusion in the schools, some children attending, some evacuated. Some male teachers had signed up and the schools, in their absence were being run by female or retired teachers.

The industrial areas and factories had been taken over for war production. The cotton mills were making uniforms, the silk production in Macclesfield was changed to making parachutes instead of glamorous clothing. The Ford factory in Trafford Park began churning out Rolls Royce engines for the fighter aeroplanes. Others were making ammunition and armaments. Trafford Park was not a long way from us and it was thought that the Germans on finding out about the industries would try to bomb it. One of the ploys to put them off was to light bonfires along Hawthorn Lane between Chorlton and Stretford to make them think that area was Trafford Park with the hope that they would drop their bombs on the playing fields before they got there.

In 1940, as the war progressed, a Fire Watchers Order was issued. Men, who had not been called up, could be compelled to watch for forty-eight hours a month. Nora also had to go on fire watch several nights a month. Her workplace, Sunlight House in Manchester, was obliged to organise from their staff a team of fire watchers who took their place on the roof when the air raid sirens were sounded. This was so dangerous but many brave people offered their services to protect everyone else. Incendiary bombs were being dropped and, if not immediately covered by sandbags, fires would start, leaving the air raid wardens to try and put them out with stirrup pumps. These fire watchers dealt with so many small fires saving the fire brigade for the larger ones.

We heard that Jewish refugees had started to arrive in Britain and were housed in hostels and supported by the local Jewish communities. Jews coming from Germany, Holland, Belgium and, France had been under threat but some people were suspicious of them thinking there might be spies among them. There were a lot of rumours going around about what was happening to the Jews in Germany and the surrounding countries. They were certainly the subject of a lot of hatred over there and things were not easy for them. The Germans made them wear a yellow star of David on their clothes to identify them as Jews. One rumour was that they were being sought out and put on trains to special work camps east of Germany.

As the Italians joined forces with Hitler suspicion was also thrown onto the Italian communities in Britain. It became time for internment and entire Italian families were housed in fenced off communities and guarded. Some internment camps were on the coast but most were sent to the Isle of Man using vacant boarding houses.

Bert discussed his situation with Nora and the fact that they were increasing the conscription age to forty-one years old. If he received his call up papers, he would have to go into the Army. He said if he volunteered, he might be able to get into the Royal Air Force instead. Nora was not happy for him to go but saw his side of the situation. Still, she did not want him to go without them being married first. Bert asked for my permission which I gave readily. They became engaged and agreed to get married before he left England. I was thrilled to bits for her. He bought her a beautiful diamond solitaire ring. They were very much in love and I did not want to see another situation like my own. Although, as yet, they did not have children, they deserved to find happiness together before he went.

As we dashed here and there arranging a marriage at short notice, Bert went to the offices of the Royal Air Force and signed up. I wrote out and posted the invitations. At 10 am on Thursday 19th October 1940 the day before Bert was thirty-five, their marriage took place with a Nuptial Mass at English Martyrs Church. Photographs were taken in a studio with his best man Tom Halton, and bridesmaids; Nora's friend Gertrude Strong and Bert's niece Margaret. Nora looked beautiful dressed in white and carrying a bouquet of lilies. How proud Harry would have been if he could have walked all his girls down the aisle.

The wedding party was held at Parkers Reception Rooms on Needham Avenue in Chorlton. We had a wonderful afternoon and evening. A bit of light relief from the war was just what was needed although several times the gentlemen seemed to gather in earnest conversation in corners and at the bar. Because it was midweek several people were unable to attend; George and Norah, Cousin Monica, Bert's sister May and her husband Fred who all sent GPO greetings telegrams to the happy couple. Even so, there were a good many there with all the Currans and all the friends they had. The wedding over, they caught the train to Blackpool for a few days honeymoon before Bert left Manchester.

Nora and Bert said they would like to make their new home living with me. This arrangement suited us all now that Bert had enlisted. Looking back, I don't think I could or would have managed without them. Thank goodness I had Nora with me during the war years. Times were so bad.

As we were not having many raids yet, we still carried on our social lives. We weren't going to let the Germans dishearten us. As well as our gas masks we had also been issued with identity cards which we had to carry with us and produce for inspection by the police if asked. Of an evening Nora sometimes came along to the Claremont Picture House with me or I went with Mrs Frost. Always before the main film, they showed the Pathe News. We saw films of our brave men and women going to France to fight the enemies. Films of our Royal Air Force fighting the German aircrafts and shooting them down. They always showed a positive side of the war encouraging us to be very patriotic, to sign up, to be frugal with everything to help the war effort, to not gossip, and to not spread information that the enemy could use.

When we came out at the end how strange it was to walk along the street without any lights. Orders had been made for all the street lights to be turned off and vehicles had to be driven without lights. Neither were there any lights from the houses, not even pale lights through curtains. If a light was seen from outside, the local Air Raid Warden, as he patrolled his streets, would come banging on the door giving you a warning. It was thought that by us staying in the dark, the pilots from Germany would not realise they were over a town. We carried a torch to use in an emergency (when the warden couldn't see us). We fixed a top guard over the torches so the light shone down and not up. Occasionally lights would suddenly flash in front of you from motor cars. They nearly blinded you after the darkness. Even the buses had to have a conductor walking in front waving a white flag to warn pedestrians. A bit like when we had the smogs and the drivers couldn't see a thing in front of them. Thank goodness nothing moved very fast! We were always bumping into someone who was dressed in dark clothing. We all took it in good spirit and apologies were thrown around all over the place.

There were public air-raid shelters built all over the City with several in Moss Side. These were brick buildings with a concrete roof in the hope that that would protect us. Some shelters were built underground sheltered with an arched corrugated iron roof covered with soil or sandbags, with entrance steps going down into the ground. These were Anderson shelters. By 1941 they had designed an indoor shelter called a Morrison shelter which consisted of a steel mesh frame the height of a table and big enough to lie in, covered by a steel plate strong enough to withhold falling debris.

If you were in the picture house or a theatre and the sirens sounded you had to leave and be directed to the nearest shelter which might be an underground tunnel or basement room. Some shelters had rows of seating along either side or if they were wide enough, they had bare bunk beds. You never knew how long a raid would last so mothers took bedding with the children in case they had to stay the night. A flask of tea and a sandwich often came in handy when we waited a long time for the all-clear sound. The sirens urgently brought all the local people together in the shelters and to keep their spirits up they often had a good old sing-song. There was always a sense of camaraderie despite those dire times. We already had good communities but the war seemed to bring out more concern for neighbours. Make no mistakes, there were still plenty of reasons to decry people. Some were happy to profit from poor situations or, being quite selfish, refused to take their turns at volunteering.

It was quite a walk from our house to the nearest shelter and I didn't like doing that in the middle of the night. Even though I knew Nora worried about me I refused to leave the house. She would not go without me and so we spent every raid sitting on the stairs down in the coal cellar, hoping any bombs would not get down to us past two flights of stairs. Nothing was going to make me leave the home I had built with Harry. It was cold and dark down there so we always had blankets close at hand to take with us. Not the best ones as we didn't want to get coal dust on them. We kept candles in metal candle holders and matches on the stairs. The kitchen was only at the top of the stairs so we could always nip up for a drink if we were there for long.

The nights that Nora was on fire watch duty were worrying. Not only did I worry about her being in the centre of Manchester, and all my other children in their homes, but I felt quite vulnerable being all alone. I felt those nights would never end. With no one to talk to, my fears for all the family escalated out of all proportion. Sometimes, I thought, if a bomb hit and the bricks fell on me, I would know how Harry had suffered in France. I never told them how much I was afraid. I could not show any weakness. I was the matriarch and strong and held the family together. If I was strong the family was strong. But when I was on my own, I said my prayers and talked to Harry.

One chilly night, having been dragged from our warm beds by the sound of the air raid sirens, we sat on the cellar stairs, wrapped in blankets, listening and praying as we heard the planes going overhead. They were probably on their way to Trafford Park. Plane after plane droned over. There were whizzing sounds and then the burst of explosives as bombs were dropped. We listened to hear if they seemed to be dropping them nearer. Mostly they were incendiary bombs intended to cause fires which could be devastating. Quietly we sat saying the Rosary together, trying to feel brave but teeth chattering at the nearness of the bombs. Then, suddenly right in front of us, there was a huge crash and blast as the window in the cellar smashed and everything shook. A red glow lit the cellar from the window and through the pinholes on the coal hole cover. Covered in coal dust, we fled as quickly as we could back up the stairs into the kitchen and out of the back door. How I got out that fast I'll never know. We could hardly breathe in our panic. I was shaking and Nora had her arms around me. I think we were both crying. We heard noise and shouting coming from the street in front and then things went quiet. A figure emerged from the house. Mr Dinsdale was our fire warden and had happened to be patrolling our street when an incendiary bomb had landed on the front step. He was extremely brave and capable and managed to put the fire out before too much damage was done. The neighbours were most concerned for us and with all our nervous chatter and endless cups of tea we never got back to bed that night. We were forever grateful to Mr Dinsdale. And, so we would never forget the bomb, we always had the dent in our front step to tell the tale.

Chapter Fourteen

Every morning as we had breakfast, we listened to the wireless for reports of any raids that had taken place the night before. This early in the war we didn't have a lot of raids and we tried to carry on as usual.

Just after the first Christmas of the war, they started to ration some of our foodstuffs. We were given ration books which we had to register with our local shops. The first to be rationed was meat. We were each only allowed 4oz of bacon and 1s 2d worth of meat a week, which would have been enough to buy two chops. There was always a plentiful supply of beef tripe which at first wasn't rationed and soon became a staple part of our diet. It was very good for you if you liked it. Cooking it slowly in milk made it quite tender. We were limited to 2oz of butter and 8oz of sugar. This was per person per week. We were encouraged to eat more easily available food like potatoes. Months later new rationing came in. We were rationed to; 2oz cheese, 4oz margarine, 4oz cooking fat, 3 pints of milk, 2oz tea, and 1 fresh egg (but we could get dried egg powder). With preserves like jam or marmalade, we were allowed a 1lb jar every 2 months, and sweets were limited to 12 oz every 4 weeks. The reason for all the rationing was to help feed our troops and allow workforces to concentrate on providing for the war effort.

All my children were now spread around and I relied on them keeping me informed as to how safe they were and whether any bombs had fallen near them. None of my grandchildren had been evacuated and Eileen was housed out in Royal Oak away from the town and industry. All I could do was pray. Kathleen lived the other side of Princess Road on Garswood Road and whenever possible her son Freddie stayed with Eileen and Sid and little Patricia in Royal Oak away from danger. None of us wanted the children to have to be evacuated. I prayed for George and Norah in Stoke on Trent with their three children, Maureen, Michael, and Eileen. As a policeman, George was exempt and had not been called up. At least he was at home with his family. I heard regularly from them by letter and I sent them lots of information about what was going on in Manchester assuring them that we were all faring well. Kathleen, my daughter in law, came to see me often bringing any news she had from Frank. He was still in North Africa and sent lots of letters home whenever he could. Sometimes she would receive two or three at once and then none for a week or two as they moved from place to place.

London took an awful punishment from the Germans with their bombs. Relentlessly night after night. Then on 21st December 1940, Liverpool was bombarded over two nights with bombing raids attacking the docks. Explosives and incendiary bombs were dropped and many of Manchester's full and part-time firefighters and Civil Defence workers were deployed to help Liverpool. Even though we were scared, we were determined to keep our chins up, carrying on as usual. These big raids were getting nearer and nearer. It could be our turn next.

On the evening of 22nd December 1940, the sirens sounded and the raids started, on this night and the next. We had heard of these two-night bombing raids over Liverpool and how it was impossible to try and get any organisation before the next bout of raids began. Bombs were now being relentlessly aimed at the centre of Manchester, explosives, and incendiary. Blowing up buildings and starting fires.

People still tried to go to work in the town after the first night's bombs but most of their places of work had been destroyed. Fires still raged as many of our firefighters hadn't returned from Liverpool. Bricks and piles of debris, where buildings had collapsed, covered the roads and pavements. Nora tried to get to work. With no transport, she had to walk there. Sunlight House, her place of work, had not taken a hit so they were able to continue working. Where buildings had been hit there was a hopeless air of despondency. Thick black clouds enveloped the skeletal buildings. Fires glowed like devil eyes out of the empty window frames. Firemen with hoses and streams of water formed dark silhouettes against the red glow. Tired fire teams who had raced back from the Liverpool bombings, arrived to be faced with Manchester's devastation. So much destruction; Piccadilly, Corporation Street, Manchester Cathedral, Free Trade Hall and the Royal Exchange, all had bomb damage. Thankfully our newly built Central Library and the Midland Hotel, at its side, had escaped any damage.

The foul smell of carnage, carried from the town to the suburbs, was everywhere. Bombed houses were still smoking and rescues were taking place recovering people, alive or dead from collapsed houses. I had to pass one unfortunate house as I hurried to visit Kathleen. Two bombs had dropped over near her home and I was worried. From the pavement outside, all rooms were on view to the public where the wall had collapsed. Paperchain Christmas decorations drooped forlornly in the breeze. A curtain hung limply on a sloping rail and in the dust and rubble, a child's shoe lay next to a small doll. It looked lonely and left behind. A present wrapped in torn dusty red Christmas paper waited in the rubble to be opened. No Christmas cheer in this empty shell of a house. I wondered whether there was anyone left who had hung these decorations ready for the festive season. I felt the guilt and relief that I and my family had escaped safely from the bombing, at least for today. I thanked God and said a prayer for the family from the bombed site.

As it grew dark on the evening of 23rd December we waited. Candles and matches, blankets, rosary beads, and torch ready on the stairs. We had eaten and were having a cup of tea in the backroom when the sirens sounded. They were earlier that night. We were scared. We had seen the terrible devastation already from last night. Please God, don't let it happen again. Like the night before, we heard the terrifying sound as wave after wave of planes droned across the sky. We sat on the cellar steps listening to the sounds as the planes flew closer, holding our breath until they had gone past or hearing the whistle of the falling bombs and then the explosions. We never slept that long night. The skies glowed red from all the fires. That could have been our last night. I prayed please God that my children were safe in their homes. I would have given anything for us all to be together on a night like that. We never knew it would be like that. It was never like that in the last war. Then it was the men in the battlefields who suffered. Now it was men, women, children. Anyone, the bombs did not discriminate.

Over those two nights, we heard that at least 500 tons of explosives and 2000 incendiaries were dropped on Manchester. The destruction was immense. Almost 700 were killed and 2000 injured. There was hardly a building in the centre of Manchester left undamaged. Blocks of warehouses, offices, theatres, banks had all fallen victim and now lay in submission and sorrow, waiting for the wisps of smoke to die away before being cleared.

It was Christmas Eve. Would they come back again? The children were expecting Father Christmas to visit, not the Germans. Now we had to pull ourselves together for the sake of the children's innocent pleasure. It was hard but families did it. We stepped over the rubble and sang our Christmas Carols with full gusto. We were not going to let them beat us.

We were Mancunians, if not by birth then by adoption and pride.

English Martyrs' church and presbytery had been hit by a bomb on the first night of the blitz. Most of the stained glass windows were destroyed and the roof broken in places. Our Christmas day Masses were held in the Retreat House of the Cenacle Convent also on Alexandra Road.

All of us, except George's family, gathered at my house on Christmas Day. Thankfully we had all been spared the physical hurts though we were all on edge in case of another raid. Surely not on Christmas Day. We ate from what our meagre rations allowed us to make. We opened up the best room, lit a roaring fire, and with sherry, and gin and orange to boost our morale, toasted absent friends. The little ones sang or recited their party pieces and received their gifts. Later as the children were settled in beds, we danced to the big band sounds on the windup gramophone, we gathered around the piano and sang songs that included carols, popular songs and some very rude songs about the Germans. False gaiety hid our fears and cares at least for one day and night. I sat in my comfy armchair and watched with such love this family Harry and I had created. Hopefully, I had carried on the Curran tradition of enjoying a loving, happy, generous family.

Chapter Fifteen

January 1941 saw Manchester in a terrible mess. As well as all the devastation, we had to cope with a cruel winter. We had such a cold spell that at times, the water froze in the pipes which supplied our houses. Nothing came from the taps. Water was at a premium. For basic use, we gathered the snow in buckets and melted it for washing. Unfortunately, when we washed the whites, we found the water contained lots of soot specks. Not surprising with the coal fires and the clouded debris from the bombs. Although it was so cold, the snow decorated the streets and houses in white innocence at least for the first few hours after the snowfall. The delivery carts soon made tracks on the cobbles and the horses drawing them along stood at our doors with rugs on their backs and clouds of steaming breath rising from their nostrils. No spare bread crusts to treat them with during this time of rationing as every crumb was eaten in our house. The delivery boys with their bread and milk were hardly recognisable inside balaclavas and scarves. Always a cheerful "Morning Missus" full of life running from cart to house and house to cart as the horses, who knew all the stopping places, stepped and stopped, moving along on their own.

There were still lots of horses and carts on the streets of Manchester and they were kept in local stables overnight. During the Blitz, just before Christmas a stable in Ancoats had been hit by an incendiary bomb and set on fire. With such a lot of straw and wood, it soon smoked and took light. It was reported in the paper that an air raid warden called William Hallam had run into the burning building, without fear for his life, and opening all the stable doors had led the horses out without any loss. Such bravery from our air raid wardens. It reminded me of how brave our local warden Mr Dinsdale was.

At least we had a roof over our head. That winter saw numbers of families homeless and having to rely on the hospitality of family or neighbours who took them in. The spirit of the people was wonderful. It didn't matter if your house was overcrowded with homeless relatives. Everyone was just so thankful to be alive. It would take more than Hitler and the Germans could throw at us to destroy our morale.

After an air raid, it took time to clear the streets of all the debris. Still, the women were out every morning with their donkey stones cleaning their steps. Every day, the dent in our step reminded us how lucky we had been.

The trams were running again so Nora didn't have to walk to work. Bert had been sent abroad with the Royal Air Force and we were never sure just where he was as, for security reasons, he was not allowed to tell us in his letters. Nora had joined the entertainment team at work, The Manchester Municipal Players, and they were preparing and practising to put on a show. She was in the chorus line of dancing girls. We all got tickets to go and watch and I was very proud of her. She would have a go at anything. All that high kicking with her legs on show! Goodness me how things had changed since I was a girl. I never showed even a glimpse of my ankles. I didn't show much more than that now. Girls were growing their hair a bit longer now and wearing it like film stars. Rita Hayworth had glorious hair, rolled over from her forehead in what the girls called "Victory Rolls". Long wavy hair was very fashionable when going out dancing but on workdays they wore it curled up tidily in a roll. Factory workers wore a scarf around it tied on top in a bow. All hair out of the way of the machines and all the dirty work. Friday night became the night all girls stayed in and washed their hair ready for their night out on a Saturday. Friday, payday, became the night that the men, who were exempt from call up, went out together for a beer or two without the women. Saturday was for meeting up, for the picture house or the dance halls. The big band sounds were popular in the dance halls, Duke Ellington, Glenn Miller, "Ha ha ha, hee hee hee. Little brown jug don't I love thee", I never could get that tune out of my head. Couples twirled around the dance floor holding on to each other for as long as possible before they were called up or returned to their regiments.

The wireless played songs to cheer us all up and during the mornings there was a programme called "Music While You Work" which was played in the factories to jolly the workers along. It also kept the housewives happy as they swept and dusted in time to the music in their homes.

Reading the newspaper one day I was surprised to see the name of the TSS Voltaire, the liner on which we had cruised. The article reported that at the beginning of the war it had been requisitioned by the Navy. On April 4th 1941 whilst patrolling the seas near Cape Verde they had been spotted by the German Ship Thor and after firing at each other for just four minutes the Voltaire was ablaze and hoisted a white flag of submission. Seventy-five sailors had been killed while one hundred and ninety-seven were rescued and taken prisoners of war on the ship Thor.

I couldn't imagine that graceful liner bedecked with guns where I had sat in my deckchair and Nora had played deck sports in the sun. How sad that the ship would sail no more. But still, we have our memories.

Mrs Curran had not been too well of late. She lived now with her daughter Helena in Mersey Bank Avenue which was a good tram or bus ride away, just before the bridge crossed the River Mersey. She was amazing, as sharp as ever in her mind, but at eighty-seven she was struggling to get about.

Because we had to pay, we rarely called a doctor. To ease our pains, we relied as much as possible on homemade remedies. If we had a sore throat, we gargled with saltwater. For coughs and colds, we drank honey and hot lemon juice, warts were rubbed with a potato skin which was then buried in the soil. For skin infections, a warm poultice of moist oats was spread on the wound and covered with a bandage. This would hopefully draw all the badness out. For toothache one answer was to put a crushed clove or oil of clove onto the tooth to numb the pain. Before we paid for a visit to a doctor, we always visited the chemist first for his advice. It was cheaper. Lots of skincare was natural as well. Face masks were made of oatmeal and honey and hair was rinsed in vinegar to make it shine.

Stockings became hard to come by in wartime so girls became inventive. As their legs were on show they tinted the skin with make-up or gravy browning, and then got a friend to draw a line down the back of their legs to look like seamed stockings. Very effective and no ladders!

Bert's father, Joseph Briggs was also feeling his age according to Bert's niece Margaret. Although he was only seventy-seven, he wasn't fairing so well as Mrs Curran who was a whole ten years older than him. Margaret came to see Nora quite a lot while Bert was abroad. She and Bert's sister Marie were looking after Mr Briggs in the family house in Longsight. They had also been lucky and had not been affected by the bombs but Margaret said every night you could see the searchlights at Belle Vue tracing the skies looking to target any German bombers.

By December Joseph Briggs was very poorly with a liver problem and on December 8th 1941 he passed away at home with Marie looking after him. Bert was unable to get leave to be with him as he was in North Africa, and was not able to be home for the funeral either. I went with Nora to St Joseph's in Longsight for his Requiem Mass and then to Moston Cemetery where he was buried in the family grave. Nellie, who had travelled from Kirkby Lonsdale, May and Marie were heartbroken. Marie had given her life to caring for her father and looking after Margaret as if she was her own. Another sad Christmas after the devastation of last Christmas. We were used to the bombings now and took the sirens in our stride.

Nora received photographs from Bert and was quite upset to see he had lost so much weight. He told her he had been quite poorly but was now getting better and putting weight back on. No doubt the death of his father must have affected him quite badly and of course, he would be worrying about Marie and Margaret on their own at home. May and her husband Fred lived in Weston-Super-Mare with Anthony and Josephine. His sister Nellie and her husband Bert had moved during the depression for work. Bert had taken a clerk's job on the Underley Estate and lived in Kirkby Lonsdale, a small village in Westmorland and although they had a lovely cottage on the estate and Bert had regular work, Nellie never got used to the countryside. She was a real town girl. Their son Albert was in the Royal Air Force like our Bert.

Although we fared well ourselves during the bombing raids and our young men were safe, we still had our share of heartache. When it came to Christmas in 1942 Harry's mother, Ellen Curran was taken ill and passed away on Christmas Eve at her daughter's house. It seemed like every Christmas there was another heartache we had to hide from the little ones. A Requiem Mass was held at English Martyrs' Church for her on December 28th and she was buried in the family grave at St Joseph's Cemetery, Moston, with her son Patrick and daughter Kathleen. This was such a loss to our big family. Her strength and determination had carried her children from Ireland to a better life here in Manchester where they all followed her example and worked hard and lived well. Her legacy lived on through her large loving family.

Over the next couple of years, I was blessed with several more grandchildren. Frank and Kathleen now had Christine. Eileen and Sid were blessed with a boy, Anthony. Kathleen and Wilf had Joan, and George and Norah had another boy Peter. Such joy but more children to worry about in those terrible times. Goodness me, my house was bursting at the seams when they all called together, it was like a nursery. We found it easier to trot them all off for a run around Alexandra Park. How lovely it was to have them all together. I loved it and I doted on each and every one of them. I was determined to keep this family as close together with each other as possible. All this new life compensating for all the terrible losses. We've done ourselves proud here Harry. We are up to nine now.

I was so pleased for Kathleen when she had managed to get a house on Wellfield Road in Royal Oak. She was just around the corner from Eileen. Close together again. Royal Oak was quite distant from anywhere. The nearest village was Northenden about two miles away with St Hilda's Catholic Church where they had to walk every Sunday to Mass but the Catholic school was on the other side of Wythenshawe Park. This was no longer a private estate as it had been given by Lord Simon to the people of Manchester for their recreation. It was either this or go to Royal Oak Primary School which was on their doorstep. This was an option they had to take but as they were from good Catholic homes and went to church on Sundays, I didn't think that was too bad.

No. I was not moving anywhere. Always it was suggested, as I only rented this so out of date house but this had been my home with Harry.

When we heard from Bert that he had been posted to Italy we already knew that Italy had been defeated by the British forces so we guessed he was not in the middle of any conflict. Much to our relief. In one of his letters, he was thrilled to tell us he had met up with his nephew Albert at one point but had both now been directed elsewhere. His letters always sounded very jolly and full of information about shows and dinners that had been put on to entertain the troops. This was a different kind of war from the First World War. Being in the RAF Bert was being posted to more countries in the world than Harry had seen. At Christmas time we were able to send telegraphic greetings to him by writing a letter and maybe adding a photograph. This was then photographed and reduced in size and sent to the troops.

As the war years progressed, we all appeared to have reduced in size with the meagre rations we were able to get. Although for some of us this diet was no different from what we had been able to afford before. We all became rather adept at reusing almost everything. Bedsheets, worn in the middle were cut down the middle and resewn edge to edge. Clothes were unpicked and redesigned or cut down for children's outfits. Toys were homemade, improvised or handed down and repainted for children. Every spare bit of soil was planted with produce to supplement our diet. We hardly ever saw imported goods as ships were targeted by the Germans at sea. A whisper would be passed from mouth to mouth, neighbour to neighbour.

"They have bananas in the greengrocers, hurry up before they are gone."

Country people seemed to fare very well and always had a quiet supply of eggs. If they kept hens, they were not entitled to an egg ration. Eileen and Kathleen sometimes brought a little something from the farms or market gardens near them. In Royal Oak and Wythenshawe rhubarb was seasonally in supply. Very nice but it took a large amount of our sugar allowance to make it edible! Children raided the apple and pear orchards and got away with as many as they could before the farmer chased them off his land.

Nora was thrilled to receive a letter from Bert telling her he had now been stationed in the Isle of Man. Surely, he would be a bit safer there. At the time we didn't know what he could be doing there but later found out that they were experimenting with a new radar system to spot planes.

By 1944 American soldiers had been stationed and trained over here for several years. The young ladies were eager for their company and the benefits they brought like sweets and nylons and plenty of money to spend. I could also see how they would enjoy the company of these fresh young men who had not yet been overseas in the thick of it. Life was an adventure to them and a chance to dance with a pretty girl. Perhaps the girls, starved of male company, were enjoying the novelty of being flattered and pampered as I had when I met Harry.

But by June they had gone. We heard they had landed with our troops over the channel in France. We all kept our fingers crossed and prayed that this time we would be able to drive the Germans back. By December the Germans were out of France and Belgium and still retreating. Our troops battled on into Germany until they met with the Russians who had been fighting the Germans from the East. In April admitting his defeat, we heard that Hitler had killed himself. Thank God the world was now rid of such an evil man. Berlin capitulated on

May 7th and on May 8th 1945 we all celebrated Victory in Europe.

I have never seen so many Union Jack flags flying from bedroom windows, waved by men and women dancing in the streets. Here in Manchester, there was a huge gathering of people celebrating in Albert Square before the town hall. The pubs were bursting at the seams and customers spread onto the streets laughing and cheering, waving flags and beer glasses in the air.

We all put in what we could afford from our food rations and set up long tables along George Street and decorated them with table cloths and flags. The children were seated at the tables and the grown-ups milled around. Such fancy food as we could manage. Celebrating into the night, dancing on the cobbles we almost forgot to put the youngsters to bed in the evening. We tried to remember what it had been like before the war started and wondered just how it could return to normal now. It would take such a long time to normalise after six years of war. We had lost the heart of our town to the bombs. We had so many homeless families crowding into relatives' houses. We had lost so many young men and women in the conflict. Men would return and want their jobs back but women were now used to doing the jobs the men had vacated. Women wouldn't want to give up the wages they had been earning. Nor would they want to give up the independence they had had for the last four or five years. Although we celebrated exuberantly there was apprehension in the air of what sort of life the future would hold.

Chapter Sixteen

Only as the German prison camps were opened did it get reported just how bad the treatment of the Jewish people had been. Pictures in the newspapers showed starving prisoners with skull-like faces smiling with gratitude for their release. Horrible, dreadful stories of the extermination of millions were reported and read with disbelief over the next months. In Britain, we rejoiced that the fighting was over and soon our war-weary men would be coming home.

Fighting was still going on in Japan and many of our men were in prison camps there. The Americans took it upon themselves to end the war quickly by dropping two atomic bombs on Hiroshima and Nagasaki with shocking results. Bombs, the like of which, we had not heard of before. The newspapers reported the dead and showed appalling photographs of fleeing children with the clothes burned from their bodies. The devastation was so immense that the Japanese surrendered to the Americans on August 15th 1945.

With the war over our troops were to be demobbed by a points system. By age and years of service. Frank and Bert returned to us with much jubilation on our part. Everywhere there were welcome home parties with bunting flying up and down the streets tied to the lamp posts. We were lucky but some not so. Mrs Shaw across the street from us had her husband return on crutches which he would always need having had one leg blown off. But thankfully he still came home.

Ever resourceful and full of fun, our Kathleen went door to door to her neighbours asking for subscriptions and organised a charabanc to take the whole street on a day trip to the seaside to celebrate. She also invited me and we had such a glorious day on the beach with all the children building sandcastles and splashing in the sea. We managed to get cones of cockles and winkles from the stalls on the beach and sat in deckchairs enjoying the sunshine and fresh air. Naughty young mums went paddling in the sea with the hems of their dresses tucked up the leg of their drawers. Goodness me I dread to think what my mother would have said.

It was strange to realise that even though he hadn't been living with us, Nora and Bert had been married for five years now. He had come home to us and we now had a man about the house all the time. It was good to see them so happy. But Bert had returned home with itchy feet after meeting so many young men from Australia and South Africa and hearing about the wonderful lives they had there. He tried to talk Nora into thinking about going abroad. Nora, thankfully, wouldn't even entertain the idea of going so far away and leaving me and the family here. What could I have done to stop them if she had wanted to go? Probably nothing, but thank goodness she was strong enough to resist.

I had already put a spanner in the works when Bert had suggested to Nora that they buy a house in Whalley Range which they could afford and had much better facilities than our home. I know she was very tempted. It was only ten minutes' walk away, near to English Martyrs' Church. She asked me if I would go and live with them if they bought it and of course I had to refuse. Once again, I was stubbornly holding onto the family home that Harry and I had put together. Any memories of him were in this house. It may not have a bath, an inside toilet, or electricity but it had happiness and memories. I wasn't going to budge. It had been Nora and me, just us two, for so many years now it seemed she just would not abandon me to live on my own. Although I felt a bit guilty, I was so happy. I would have been devastated to be left on my own if they went. I knew I had lots of family members who came to see me often but it would have been a very sad home on my own.

Bert was working back at his old job as a shipping clerk and went off each morning with his trilby hat and gaberdine overcoat over his suit. His black shoes were immaculately polished and if it was raining, he would wear rubber galoshes over them. He would walk to Princess Road and catch a bus into Piccadilly. They were trying to make the centre of Manchester look a bit better and had erected ten-foot-high hoardings around the bombed-out buildings until they could be reconstructed. They had colourful advertisements pasted on them which brightened things up a bit. There was certainly plenty of reconstruction to do.

We weren't short of German prisoners of war around the area and they were being used to help with the building of whole estates of prefabricated houses for the homeless families. They were just single storey with a couple of bedrooms, a living room, kitchen, and bathroom. Ideal for them. They were also laying out new roads in Wythenshawe, up near Eileen and Kathleen, ready for the building of new houses by Manchester Corporation to be rented out to families as they cleared the slums. Money was being ploughed into getting the country back to normal. Eileen's husband had plenty of work as a bricklayer as the new estates started to be built in Baguley and Newall Green. Manchester had bought the Wythenshawe Estate from Cheshire for overflow housing a while back and now had the permission to build. Such beautiful two storey houses with all the modern conveniences you could need. They all had gardens, front and back, with hedges and trees. All beautifully landscaped. Unlike the straight lines of terraced houses in Moss Side the roads curved round with so many small drives and avenues, it was very easy to lose your directions. This was to be the biggest housing estate in Europe.

Although there was a lot of animosity towards the German prisoners of war, those who got to know them said they were only young men, the same as ours, who had been called up by Hitler and had no choice but to fight the war. Now the war was over they were allowed out of camp on Sundays to visit any families who invited them for a meal. Many of them were now hoping to stay here where they had settled into the work they had been put to.

With all the young men returning from the fighting and getting back to normal life, there was an outbreak of pregnancies. That was no surprise. It was not long before Nora and Bert told me their most welcome news that they were expecting a baby in the following May. I was so pleased for them. Nora was the last to start her family. She was now thirty-three and Bert was forty. She blossomed in pregnancy with never a day's sickness like some girls. They carried on their social lives meeting up with friends at the tennis club and going to whist drives at church. They weren't people who went to public houses. They did have a couple of drinks with friends; gin and orange or sherry, and that was usually at parties or social occasions.

Bert didn't want Nora to have their baby at home so they arranged for her to go into St Mary's Hospital opposite the Palace Theatre in Manchester. Towards the end of May her labour started and she spent time pacing the hospital corridors thinking her baby would never arrive. But on May 27th 1946 Joan Elizabeth was born to much rejoicing. "Monday's Child is fair of face." Once again, I was a new Grandma and this time the baby would be brought up in my house. Our Kathleen already had a daughter Joan and to distinguish between them, Nora's little girl was always called Joan

Elizabeth. Nora and Bert shared the back bedroom, which had always been Nora's room, and put Joan Elizabeth's cradle in with them. I still had my lovely big front bedroom which stretched the whole width of the house. I got plenty of cuddle time with our new baby when I suggested Nora have a little nap in the afternoons.

Now we were off again and Frank and Kathleen were also expecting. They had another girl, Pauline, a sister for Christine. They would bring the two girls to see me whenever they could and our Kathleen, who was working for C & A Modes, would bring her Joan to us for Saturdays whilst she worked. Our house had changed once again from being a quiet, grown-up place to a house of babies and toys, with terry-towelling nappies airing on the rack. I loved it.

Joan Elizabeth was growing up such a bonny baby. Her short blonde hair was coaxed into a curly quiff which took ever such a lot of effort. About the time she was fourteen months old, Nora and Bert announced that they were expecting another baby. And then Eileen and Sid also announced their pregnancy. Goodness, I found it hard to keep up with them all.

I felt I wanted to enjoy the older children as much as I could before they grew up so with Mrs Frost and our Kathleen, we arranged to almost take over a guest house in Rhyl for a holiday with them all. George drove his children over from Stoke. Eileen's children; Patricia and Anthony, Kathleen's Fred and Joan, and Frank's Christine all came with us on the train. This was excitement in itself for the children who had never been on a steam train before. They kept opening the carriage windows and had to quickly shut them as the train hooted to warn us that we were coming to a tunnel. Just in time before all the smoke would have entered the carriage. Once again, I was managing to keep all my family as close as

I could and the children had such a great time. They made their own fun and games together without much direction from the grown-ups. They played together and got to know each other really well. Donkey rides, bike and, tricycle hire along the wide promenade, sandcastle competitions, and paddling in the sea whilst we adults lazed in deckchairs watching them. Then back to the digs where the landlady would have a lovely tea prepared for us. We had to let her have our ration books for the week as some things were still on ration. Quite a few things especially sweets stayed rationed until 1953.

We tried to arrange this holiday with all the children every year from then on as they loved it and it gave their parents a break. We were lucky to be able to afford it but we saved up all year to have this holiday.

At home, I had started to take a bit of a back seat now Nora and Bert ran the house. I was glad to take it a bit easier as my legs and ankles were always swelling up and I was quite often out of breath if I did too much. I wasn't the slimmest of people by any means so that didn't help either. Anyway, Nora would do the housework in the mornings and I would watch over Joan Elizabeth. Then when we had had dinner, I would push the pram to Alexandra Park to watch the bowling whilst Nora sat down and relaxed as she listened to Woman's Hour on the wireless. I knew lots of people at the bowling green and followed their games avidly, sometimes marking their cards for them if they had a match on. I still played bowls sometimes and I was still a vice president. Nora always made sure, in the late afternoon when her work was done, to wash and change into fresh clothes, and put on her lipstick before Bert came home from work.

Alexandra Park was always such a draw for me after all the strolls Harry and I had taken there in the early days of our marriage. If it was the weekend, I would take any other visiting cousins with me to the park. We would take some spare crusts so we could feed the ducks. If Nora and Bert were playing in a tennis match, I would walk the pram to the tennis club and watch them and then wander around the park, to the cactus house or the café. I used to see so many people I knew that it would take me all afternoon to get around. By which time Joan Elizabeth would be awake and sat up peeping around the hood to see who I was talking to.

Barbara was born on July 15th 1948 and because Nora had already had a hospital birth, she was told she was alright to have a home birth. Of course, they didn't want that, and Bert insisted that she go to a nursing home. There was a nursing home nearby which was run by an order of nuns and they got a place for her there. She stayed there for two weeks before she brought Barbara home. I had Joan Elizabeth to myself for all that time as children were not allowed to visit. I had also had to go back to doing the housework; that was hard work again. So now when she came home the baby's cradle was put in their room and I suggested that Joan Elizabeth's cot be moved into my bedroom for more space.

The first Sunday home, we had Barbara's christening at English Martyrs' Church as Joan Elizabeth's had been. Christenings were always done as soon as possible after birth. Partly because so many babies didn't survive and partly because tradition said that Mothers were not to be in public until they had been blessed to cleanse them. Quite a social occasion with everyone in their best Sunday clothes and then back to our house for refreshments. All the family was there and lots of Nora and Bert's friends.

Once Nora got back to her old self, they started to go to the whist drives at church again. Nora's hands were quite red and sore from all the washing, housework, and peeling vegetables in the sink. She didn't think they looked very nice for displaying them on the table as they played cards. Following one of my handy hints, she would rub them with lemon to make them whiter and then drench them with glycerine and rose water, covering them overnight with little cotton gloves. Just as I had done as a young girl working in service. There was certainly an improvement the next day.

Since Nora had been away from home for two weeks in the Nursing Home, Joan Elizabeth always worried when her Mum went out. Nora promised to bring a little present back trying to pacify her. As they went out in the evening, I took Joan Elizabeth to the window to wave to them. But when they got to the corner and turned and waved goodbye, she burst into tears. She didn't like them leaving her. I suppose she was too young to understand where they had gone and that they would be back before she woke. So that she didn't wake Barbara up I took her into my bedroom and gave her a cuddle and a story before she fell asleep and I put her in her cot.

Chapter Seventeen

The light was just beginning to show around the edge of the heavy curtains and the house was quiet. I listened to the birdsong and thought about the very early mornings in Southsea in my attic room. Such a lifetime ago. So much had happened since then.

The moment was disturbed by the sound of a horse and cart clattering over the cobbles. It woke up Joan Elizabeth. Her cot was pushed against the side of my bed with a blanket over one rail to keep away the draught from the empty fireplace. She opened one eye and peeped at me. Her covers had come off and she shivered. She stood up and gazed over the cot rail and smiled at me. It was easy for her to climb over the rail and onto the bed where I lay tucked under the crisp white sheets and satin bedspread. Just my head showing with the hairnet keeping my greying hair in place. We loved this time of day when she could slip into the bed and snuggle up to me and I would have her to myself. That comforting cosiness of her little body next to mine. I put my arm around her and drew her to me. The warm smell of her baby powder engulfed me as my lips touched her soft cheek.

"Tell me one of your stories Grandma, please" she whispered. How she loved her Grandma and the stories I told. I thought of all the stories I could tell her. What a life I had led.

As Christmas approached, I was told, that once again Nora and Bert were expecting another baby. They were certainly making up for the lost time of the war. Two girls, would they have a boy this time? I knew Nora was hoping for a boy.

This year our usual Christmas with all the family meant we were now bursting at the seams. George and Norah also came from Stoke with all their family, some of them staying over for a couple of days to see me. I didn't get a chance to see George's children that often. Michael always made me laugh as he took pride in being the one to go to the corner shop of an evening with a jug to buy "Grandma's Medicine". I don't think anyone ever told him how medicinal that jug of stout was! Yes, I loved a nice glass of stout in the evenings as I sat and listened to the radio, and now it was quite a relaxing habit. Harry would have laughed at me because I didn't like it when I was younger.

As with every Christmas before, after dinner, we would sit in the best room. A roaring fire in the grate warming and cheering the room that hadn't been used since the Christmas before. Chairs spread all around the room for adults, with children sitting on the floor whilst all the grandchildren took their turn to entertain before being given a Christmas present from the Aunties. Christine always obliged us by reciting the whole of "The Night Before Christmas" by heart. Joan and Patricia made a great double act imitating the comedians Hylda Baker and "Cynthia" from the radio show.

It seemed to be the thing that they all asked Auntie Norah if they could sit on her knee knowing that she would always say "I haven't got any knees". She was only small and had such short legs that when she sat down it did appear so. As it grew dark, we lit the candles which were clipped onto the end of the branches of the artificial Christmas tree which stood in the corner of the room. We were always wary of anyone going near the little flames in case their hair or clothes caught fire.

Six months later, on June 27th 1950, Nora was taken to the nursing home as she went into labour. Bert was not allowed to stay with her so he kept himself busy at home nervously helping with Joan Elizabeth and Barbara. We waited and waited for news and then Bert went across the road to the garage on the corner. They had a telephone and he asked could he phone the nursing home from there. I can picture him now as he came leaping and shouting across the cobbles waving his arms, so unlike Bert, shouting

"It's a boy. It's a boy."

Oh, how happy we all were to have a baby boy in the house.

But what was he to be called? Bert wanted him to be called Neil and Nora wanted to name him after Dennis O'Mahony. Well, what do you think? Nora got her own way again and he was called Dennis Neil. Such a nice name.

When Dennis was born Nora and Bert moved their bedroom up to the top of the house with Dennis in the cradle. The room behind mine became the bedroom for Joan Elizabeth who now had a bed and Barbara who was in the cot. It didn't matter that they were in another room from me. They still climbed out of bed and sneaked in with me for stories in the morning.

Quite often I would take them up and put them to bed at night if Nora was seeing to Dennis, or Bert had just come home for his tea. We still had no lights upstairs not even gas lights. I had to carry a candle holder with a lit candle so we could see where we were going as well as holding onto the bannister as I struggled with the stairs. As I kept my eyes on each step there was suddenly a crackling and burning smell and I realised that I had touched Joan Elizabeth's long hair with the lighted candle and singed it. It smelled awful as I quickly patted it to make sure it wasn't still alight. I hoped she wouldn't say anything but you know what children are like. I had to apologise to Nora and Bert.

That year as our Kathleen, my friend Mrs Frost, and I were once again going to Rhyl for a holiday with all the cousins, I decided to take Joan Elizabeth as well. She could share the bedroom with Kathleen and her cousin Joan. She was four years old and the youngest so I hoped she would mix in with them alright. I needn't have worried. She was already used to playing with cousin Joan at my house and they had great fun together on the donkeys and tricycles, and the beach. She was quite used to being looked after by me anyway. What a lovely time having all the young ones around me. I loved to watch them having fun and to feel so proud of them all. My children had all raised them well to be happy polite kind children. It must have been my good example!

Whilst we were in Rhyl, I took the opportunity on a Sunday to go and visit the Benedictine nuns at Gronant Abbey. I would go in time for Sunday Mass and then spend some quiet time in their gardens. In the middle of the open countryside away from the bustle of the seafront, I would have some me-time. Relaxing in the sunshine, listening to the birdsong, breathing in the country air it all felt so peaceful. Such a tonic for the spirit. Sometimes one of the nuns would offer me a cup of tea and have a chat with me. They were always ready to listen and offer helpful advice. Such cheerful and positive people with a wonderfully humble and charitable outlook on life. They were a joy to meet. With spirits lifted I made my way back to the family with a renewed love in my heart for them all.

Back home again after our lovely holiday, it was good to catch up with the little ones. Dennis had dark curly hair like Barbara. Nora was thrilled to bits with the curls which she tweaked and twirled up into a coxcomb. I think she wanted them all to be like little Shirley Temple. Poor Joan Elizabeth with her fair straight hair, which refused to be curled, thought she was very plain next to Barbara and Dennis.

When it came to Dennis being on solids, I was able to help out and had to be quite firm with him as he waved his arms all over the place sending the spoon and food flying around the room. Only one thing to do. Take him prisoner. Tucking one of his arms behind my back and holding onto his other arm, I spooned the food in. Such a little fighter. As I was doing this the girls would sit at the table in the back room and listen to "Listen with Mother" with Daphne Oxenford singing nursery rhymes and telling a story. Nora was usually still busy in the kitchen so it became listen with Grandma. When it finished, I asked them to be very nice and quiet while Nora then listened to Woman's Hour. She hadn't talked while they listened so they had to be fair.

It was then, of course, off to the park. On my own, I did have my hands full taking them to the park in the afternoon. If it was school holidays, we might also have Joan with us for the day. Joan Elizabeth sometimes rode her Raleigh Rudge three-wheeler bike with a metal carrier on the back. She was thrilled to have got this for her birthday. She had worked so hard to get it; drank all her milk to get the white bits, ate all her cabbage for the silver bits, and ate her meat for the red bits. This would eventually get passed down among them after repainting as had the dolls pram which appeared for Barbara last Christmas painted a different colour from what it had been when it belonged to Joan Elizabeth.

At the end of our back yard, there was the outside toilet. Joan Elizabeth and Barbara were sent down there on their own every evening before they went to bed. Joan Elizabeth was big enough for the toilet and Barbara sat on her potty. For toilet paper, the old newspaper had been cut into squares and threaded onto a thick piece of string. There was always half a story to read while you were there and if it was a good story you had to root through the other pieces of paper for the continuation! They never complained about going out there, except for the one night when they screamed the place down.

They sounded really frightened. We leapt up and dashed out to see what had happened. Had someone come through the back gate? Had some animal got in under the door? Pushing the door open we saw them sat there in pitch-black darkness, terrified as the nightlight candle had blown out. What a relief. They didn't like it when we laughed at them.

When their cousin Joan came on a Saturday they often played in the yard. Joan liked to draw and on one occasion she had brought some of her chalks to use on the paving flags in the yard. Spotting an opportunity, she drew a big Red Indian Chief with a large multicoloured feather headdress on the toilet door. Well, that was it, Joan Elizabeth refused point-blank to even go in the yard, never mind the toilet until the chalked figure had faded away. She never forgot that and although we couldn't stop laughing at her I had to ask Joan not to draw frightening pictures again.

Eileen and Sid had been very lucky and managed to get one of the newly built houses on the Wythenshawe estate at Newall Green. It had three bedrooms which they needed now because Patricia was growing up and they also had Anthony and Geoffrey. They had a bathroom upstairs and a separate room for the toilet which was also upstairs.

We all went to visit in the spring. It was on the main road and looked out over the fields in front of it. It was like living in the countryside. Of course, I would have loved it. With all its modern fittings it was a luxury compared to mine but I wasn't letting on. Eileen was devastated that little country mice had come in the house and nibbled all the Easter Eggs she had put up on the shelf. The look of horror on Nora's face was a picture.

For one reason or another, the holiday in Rhyl wasn't taking place the next year so Nora and Bert decided that I should go on holiday with them to Filey on the East Coast.

Billy Butlin had built a holiday camp there before the war to provide cheap holidays for families. During the war, the camp had been requisitioned by the RAF as a military camp but by 1945 it was back to being a holiday camp again. It might have been because it had been an RAF base that Bert was attracted to it. We were able to get a train from Manchester almost to the gates of the camp which was very convenient.

What a surprise this place was. We were put up in chalets with bunk beds. That was about all there was in the room. For washing facilities and toilets we had to go to a purpose-built block a short walk away. One day Nora went to the toilets and was away ages. When she came back, she said they had waited and waited for a toilet to be available but no-one came out. By this time there was a long queue. Realising that someone had locked all the toilet doors from the inside they had to go and get a handyman with a ladder to climb over the top and unlock them all.

It was quite a while later that Joan Elizabeth and Barbara accidentally confessed to me what had happened. Whilst Barbara waited for Joan Elizabeth, they decided she should keep busy by locking the cubicles from the inside and crawling under the doors, doing the same to each one. They had no intention of being naughty, it was just something to pass the time. Such inventiveness from little minds.

There was non-stop entertainment which everyone felt obliged to join in with starting with the loudspeakers first thing in the morning

"Wakey, wakey, good morning campers".

This was our signal to get up and go to the refectory for breakfast where we all sat at long canteen tables. During the day members of the entertainment team were constantly rounding us up to take part in competitions; swimming, races, beauty queen, bonny baby, glamorous grandma, knobbly knees, muscle man, dancing, or fancy dress. All good fun but quite exhausting.

They had special activities for children so you could leave them there for a few hours. We had to try so hard to get Joan Elizabeth to go. She didn't want to go as she was quite shy of the other children she didn't know and Barbara wasn't old enough. We finally got her to go with one of the bigger girls. Even though Barbara wasn't old enough to join in that group it didn't stop her from having fun, and on her own. The first day we managed to lose sight of her and we were all panicking. There was a big fence right around the camp so we knew she couldn't get out. We dashed all over the place looking for her and to our great surprise, we spotted her right up high, riding on the wooden seat on the back of a huge elephant. She was having the time of her life with not a care in the world. She was only three!

We did have a lovely time. The food was very nice even if it was in a canteen-like dining room. Nora and I had a quiet snigger together about the difference between this and our cruise. Still, it's always better when someone else is making your meals for you and doing the washing up don't you think. In the evenings they even laid on baby patrols who walked up and down the rows of chalets listening for crying babies. Parents were able to put the children to bed and then go to a show, go dancing or have a drink in the bar. In each show or bar, there was a message board that lit up and told parents that a baby was crying and which number chalet it was in so they could go back and settle them.

There was a boating lake at Filey and Nora decided to take Joan Elizabeth and Barbara for a boat ride. Bert and I looked after Dennis in his pram and sat watching them. Nora put the two little girls into a rowing boat, sitting at one end, and then she got in and took up the oars. We couldn't help laughing at them. As Nora sat down the other end of the boat went up in the air and the girls were holding on for dear life. They looked terrified but Nora just laughed and started rowing around the lake. They didn't ask to go on it again.

Chapter Eighteen

At home, on Sunday mornings we would all go to church at English Martyrs or to the new church, Our Lady's, which had been built on Raby Street in 1949. Our Lady's was much nearer for us to walk to. I would have preferred to go to English Martyrs but had to admit it was better for my legs which had started to ache when I walked any distance. My ankles were always so swollen.

Bert would polish all the shoes on a Saturday night, including my black laced, heeled shoes. If the weather was promising to be good then summer shoes had to be ready polished or whitened as well. We always sat near the front so the children could see what was happening in the Mass. Barbara very proudly sat there reciting the Hail Mary at the top of her voice until Nora had a quick, quiet word with her.

"No talking in Church."

Everyone was sniggering. They always had to be very well behaved in front of people.

The rest of the day at home was quiet and relaxed as a Sunday should be. Bert would go to the early Mass and then cook breakfast for us all when we got home. It was not permitted to work on a Sunday and it should be given over to thinking of your faith. But then there were the Sunday Papers to read with all the gossip, the roast dinner to be prepared, and The Billy Cotton Band Show on the wireless. You could time things perfectly; just as Billy Cotton started his show with

"Wakey, Wakey"

Nora would shout

"Dinner's ready".

A hot roast beef dinner followed by pudding or fruit pie with custard. Time to relax but not for long. Tea time was cold salad, a slice of bread with "best butter" followed by tinned fruit with Carnation Milk. The portion sizes were not large or we would never have been able to eat all that. Yes, Sunday was quite special.

At the end of George Street, which had now been renamed Criccieth Street, on a Sunday morning, we were always visited by the Salvation Army Band. They set up at the corner and began singing and playing their brass instruments. Always Joan Elizabeth, who loved the sound of the band, begged to go out and watch them but it wasn't allowed. They weren't Catholics and we weren't allowed to join in with any other religious parties. Rules were rules.

As a young lady, Nora had been very disappointed when her good friend from work had asked her to be a bridesmaid at her wedding. It wasn't in a Catholic Church and she had to ask permission from our parish priest. The answer was no she couldn't and he wouldn't even allow her to attend the church service. I know I love being a Catholic and love my faith but sometimes the rules seem to be more important than anything else. She would have loved to oblige her friend but sadly had to let her down. Her friend must have felt upset and insulted. I'm sure I would.

Sweets were still rationed in those days and of course, now we had rations for three adults and three children so every Friday night Bert would take an old shoebox and the ration book and go around the corner to the sweet shop owned by Miss Cunio. Miss Cunio had lost two brothers in the war and ran the shop herself. It was always exciting and the children jumped around Bert trying to see what sweets he had managed to get for us all in the box. There would be jelly babies, dolly mixtures, cough candy, and milk chocolate.

When I went out walking with the children and the pram, we sometimes bumped into Mr Dinsdale who had been our air raid warden. He always, always offered me and Joan

Elizabeth a sugared almond from a little paper bag. We always, always politely took one but Joan Elizabeth didn't like them, they were too hard. Every so often we would buy a small bag of them to give back to him as we knew he was sharing his rations.

Nora and Bert used their furniture coupons to buy a beautiful dining room suite. A large extending table with big bulbous legs and six dining chairs. They kept it in the front room as we didn't use that room. Every week Nora would take the polish and dusters and polish it with much love and pride, and Joan Elizabeth, who wanted to help, would have the job of polishing the big round legs. That was a good trick Nora, saving yourself from crawling under the table.

On February 20th 1951 I was seventy years old. Gosh, I didn't realise I was that old. I wanted to celebrate with all our family but we had so many now that we wouldn't all fit in the house so we hired a function room and celebrated there. We had a wonderful time and during the celebrations, Pauline and Joan Elizabeth came into the room carrying a large basket of fruit with a hooped handle and covered in shiny cellophane. They walked so carefully across the room looking quite shy in front of everyone and presented it to me. I was given such a lot of delightful presents and cards from everyone I knew. The next day I took great pleasure in sitting opening them and reading all the kind and generous messages inside. They covered every surface; windowsills, piano, mantelpiece, and sideboard. I am so lucky to have so many friends and such a lovely family.

In May after my seventieth, Joan Elizabeth was five and was able to go to school. She started at Bishop Bilsborrow School on Princess Road, right next to the Bus Depot. Mrs Shaw across the road had a daughter Ann, the same age, who started school with her. Like Nora, she also had younger children and they all played together outside on the steps of our houses and the cobbled street. Once the delivery carts and horses had been in the morning there was no traffic to worry about. We made sure they never went down the alleyways at the back of the houses. You never knew who was down there. The front door was always open for them to go in and out and once Joan Elizabeth came flying in and along the hall frightened to death because she had heard thunder. I told her it was nothing, just God moving his furniture around in heaven or banging his drum. I brought her a chair and put it in front of the open door, and told her to watch for the lightning then count until the thunder started to rumble and that was how far away the storm was. After that day she never seemed to mind as much and always asked for the chair so she could watch the rain.

There were times when I tricked her and upset her, although I didn't mean to. On one occasion she was playing in the back yard and came dashing up the kitchen steps to tell me she had found a big juicy slug on the stone flags. We had seen the slugs in the alleyways at the back gate and she had been fascinated by the silver trail they left. I told her to put some salt on it and it would be twice as big in the morning. I never gave it another thought until the next morning when she dashed out to see if it had grown and found a dried-up mess in its place. She was most put out and disappointed. I felt terrible having tricked her but thought she would have forgotten about it in the morning.

There was a post office just near Bishop Bilsborrow school and on a Friday when we picked Joan Elizabeth up from school, I would treat her and Barbara to a halfpenny holy picture from the shop. They loved to choose for themselves and collect lots of different ones to put in the pages of their prayer books.

Joan Elizabeth came home from school one day with a scraped knee. She said she had fallen in the playground on the cinders and hadn't told anyone. We cleaned it up but it must have still had dirt inside it because, in the end, we had to have a visit from the doctor when it became infected. He told us to make a warm poultice with oats and wrap it around her knee with bandages to draw out the infection. We had to keep changing it every day until it looked clean enough to just bandage it. The poor little girl would sit there almost shaking, with tears in her eyes knowing that the bandage would probably be dried to the wound and have to be eased painfully away before bathing it again.

We had the National Health Service by then so we didn't have to pay for the doctor, either to visit him or for him to come to see us at home. We still felt so respectful and grateful to the doctors. Dr Redmond, our wonderful family doctor, had his practice on Princess Road and his waiting room was in the front room of his house. Chairs stood right around the room with a large dining table in the middle. You put your name in the book on the table as you arrived and as each patient went in to see him, we all moved along one chair at a time so we knew who was next. The surgery was always full of people taking advantage of the fact that now we had the NHS they didn't have to pay a fee anymore.

Dr Redmond, on one occasion, when he examined me, warned me that my circulation was not as good as it should be. It was quite a shock but then I thought about Pa and how he had died of heart failure. I realised how much I had started to slow down. This was how Pa had been when he wasn't able to come to my wedding or be left alone at home. It worried me for a while but no good was to come of that so I would just have to get on with it. I didn't want the family to start making a fuss. It made me feel strange for a while and

155

made me start looking back at the life I had had up until now. I'd always battled my way along. Facing up to obstacles, big and small, and found ways to surmount them. There is always an answer if you look hard enough. This time the answer would be with my family and the help I would be needing in the future but I didn't want to burden them with that yet.

Chapter Nineteen

I have been stuck in my bedroom for weeks now. It seems like months but it was just after Christmas when I last went downstairs. I have become the burden I didn't want to be. I have to rely on Nora and Bert for everything from bedpan to helping me wash. I have to have my meals in bed as I can't get downstairs anymore. My legs are so painful and swollen and anything I try to do leaves me breathless.

Nora helps me get sorted in the morning after she's taken Joan Elizabeth to school with Barbara and Dennis in the pram. It's nice to have a few minutes chatting with her watching little Barbara, with her mop of dark curls, playing in the room while Dennis sleeps in the pram downstairs. I try to read the paper during the day. It's usually Bert's from yesterday that he brought home with him. I can't see to read it properly in the evenings. It's starting to get lighter in the evenings, but I still have to rely on candlelight from soon after tea. The days seem to stretch out forever as I sit and look around the room. The sunshine greets me through the windows in the morning and smiles its way around the room brightening the wallpaper in shifting slices, polishing the tallboy and wardrobe, and catching little flecks of dust in its beam until it slides down and I am just left with gloom.

My days are brightened up when I get visits from Eileen and little Geoffrey during the week, or Frank or Kathleen at the weekend. They sometimes manage to visit on a Wednesday when the shops close early or later after work. It is lovely to catch up with what all the families have been doing and how the children are getting on at school. But it tires me and it doesn't take much for me to give in to a little nap in the afternoons.

We haven't had snow here this year yet. Not like last year when it seemed to be snowing right through the winter. It is frosty though and when my curtains are drawn open in the mornings, I can see the leafy patterns on the windows before the sun melts them. Sometimes it's on the inside of the pane it is so cold. I drink my morning cup of tea then slide down and wait in my warm covers until Nora lights a fire in the grate in my bedroom or lights the oil stove which gives off a lovely patterned glow around the room. Either fire soon makes it lovely and warm in my room.

Last week, on 6th February 1952, we had the awful news that our hardworking, lovable King George V1 had died. It was such a shock he was only fifty-six. Princess Elizabeth was on tour in Uganda, Africa at the time and had to be brought back to us as our new Queen Elizabeth 11 although she won't be crowned until a year has passed in mourning for her father. We will have a new Queen to emulate our wonderful Queen Victoria. We started twelve days of mourning for him immediately and flags are being flown at half-mast all over the country. Bert said quite a crowd had gathered in mourning outside the town hall in Albert Square during the day. I thought about the way we mourned Victoria when I lived in Southsea. Such a long time ago.

Joan Elizabeth always runs upstairs to see me when she comes home from school. She tells me she is quite good at her reading now. I received a letter from my friend in Portsmouth this morning and asked her to read it to me. It was quite a surprise that she did so well reading it even with it being handwritten.

Still, she loves to sit and listen to my stories, and she and Barbara still creep into my room in the mornings at the weekend and climb on my bed to hear them. They snuggle in one each side and I make up stories about anything, even the man climbing up the telegraph pole outside. They like the big pictures on my bedroom wall and I have told them they can have the two pictures of Jesus they have chosen; The Good Shepherd and the Light of the World. It's lovely to see my faith being carried on in the grandchildren.

I have to receive Holy Communion at home now when Fr Clark can come and see me. Nora sets up a little altar on my dressing table with a Crucifix, two candlesticks in glass candle holders, and some clean water for him to wash his fingers. He always has some time to talk with me and to hear my confession first, although I don't get much chance to be sinful now. I miss Fr Rowan from English Martyrs. He had been like part of our family since my moving to Moss Side and I would love to be having some conversations with him now. I would have been able to confide in him my fears and worries and he would have understood and consoled me. Some things you just can't confide even in those who are so close to you.

It's funny how, when you have time and silence on your hands, you get to go through all your old memories. All the old treasured ones; childhood with my Mama and Pa, meeting and walking out with Harry on Southsea Promenade, our lovely children as babies. Sometimes forgotten memories suddenly jump out at me; my first day in service with my uniform so big on my fourteen-year-old body; the time Harry bought me a rose when we were out walking. I kept it in a vase in my room for such a long time, it faded and dried but I couldn't bring myself to throw it away. It was a sign of Harry's love.

Bert has rigged up a bell in my room so I can just press it and it will ring downstairs if I need anything. What a help for us all that is. I can't shout loud enough for them to hear me downstairs if I need them and they have to keep running upstairs to see if I am ok. I feel like a grand old lady with servants below stairs. How times have turned around.

Wednesday 20th February 1952 is bitterly cold and frosty but I am nice and cosy in here. It is hard to believe it is actually a year since my seventieth birthday. Another one has suddenly crept up on me. I'll be spending this one in bed, I just haven't any strength to get up. Seventy-one. Such an age. I have opened all my cards and Nora has decorated every surface in my bedroom with them. All the family called to see me at the weekend so the children could celebrate with me. I lost count of how many times we had to light the candles on my cake for the children to have a go at blowing them out for me. George and his family all came up from Stoke as well. It was good to see him and the children. They live in the police station at Tunstall now and sometimes have prisoners in the cells in the building.

"I don't think I would like that," I told him but he just laughed at me.

Such a lot of flowers. Vases of tulips and daffodils and scented lilies in every direction. Joan Elizabeth made me laugh as she thought I was having another birthday today after last weekend. Nora laughed and told her I was allowed another one because I wasn't well.

"I have another present for you Mother. Can you guess?" Nora smiled.

"You're going to be a Grandma again. Bert and I are expecting another baby in September."

What a lovely surprise. How are we all going to fit in this house?

Chapter Twenty

The girls seem to be here every day lately. I've been feeling quite poorly with a high temperature and cold. I am not surprised with this weather. But then I remember I haven't been out. Perhaps I have caught a cold from a visitor on my birthday. My chest is hurting and it's very stuffy in here.

I wake up to the sound of a horse and cart on the cobbles outside making a delivery. Is it the milkman or the baker? I must go and open the door for Mrs Holbrook's delivery. No that's not right, I thought I was in Southsea. The curtains are open a tiny bit and a beam of light reaches towards the flowers on the tallboy. They are still quite fresh from my birthday. It must be about ten o'clock. Nora came up earlier but I couldn't eat any breakfast.

Is that a car outside? We don't get many of those on our street. Dr Redmond comes into my room with Nora. He is very chatty whilst he gets his stethoscope out of his medicine bag. Listening to my chest, and taking my pulse, he smiles and pats my hand. He is going to come again to see me in the morning. It's such a struggle to breathe and my chest feels sore and tight. I must be quite poorly. Nora said she would bring me a drink when she has seen Doctor out. I lie still when he's gone. I am really tired.

I must have dozed off again. I thought I was in Emsworth sitting with Mama, looking over the grassland to the sea. I could definitely smell the sea, so fresh and salty. Those beautiful days in the sunshine and clear air. Happy days with Mama and Pa. I could hear Ann Belle and little James playing out with their friends. Happy laughter.

Nora brought me a warm drink of tea and some soup for my dinner but I only managed a little drop. She sat and chatted with me for a while. She spoke of the good times we had when we went on our cruise. That was a really good memory I hadn't thought of for a while. Just us two behaving like grand ladies, eating posh food with classy people. What a time we had.

She said Eileen would be here soon.

It was the anniversary of Harry's death on 1st March. How I miss him. He was just thirty-six years old, thirty-six years ago. When did I last see him? Two days before Christmas. Just after Frank's first birthday. My treasured husband was walking to the corner in his uniform, waving and blowing kisses to us all. My eyes burned into him with love. Why didn't I grab him and cling to him and stop him going? I couldn't of course. He belonged to the army.

Two days to Christmas, children running around, excited for the arrival of Father Christmas, warm fires, Christmas decorations.

Two days to Christmas, young British men trudging through mud, marching the trails trodden by horses and gun carriages. Cold army rations, damp tents, harsh orders. Fire, fire, fire! German enemy over the ridge.

Two days to Christmas, young German men trudging through mud, marching the trails trodden by horses and gun carriages. Cold army rations, damp tents, harsh orders. Fire, fire, fire! Just the same as our young men with children at home waiting for Christmas.

Christmas Day, no guns, silence, voices raised in carols, and songs. Hasty Christmas service on improvised altars. English and German, all the same. What a waste of lives, spoiler of lives. We don't learn. We did it all again. God save our children from any more.

Is it Eileen or Kathleen? You do sometimes confuse me, you girls. I thought at first it was Nana Curran, you are so like her. Oh, its Kathleen, I can always tell when you laugh. Are you still being naughty? Have you been sliding on the ice in the park? Is the lake frozen again? Who's to blame this time? You run rings round me you rascals. I wouldn't have it any other way, you are such fun. Do you remember those lovely Friday nights when all your friends came to our house for a knees-up? Those were good times.

I keep drifting off to sleep. I can still hear them chatting around my bed. Such irrelevant conversation; the price of bread, new dresses in the shops. It's comforting listening to their voices.

Is Eileen coming today, she's usually here by now, isn't she?

Someone is serving tea. I can hear the spoons stirring in the teacups. I'll have Alice read the tea leaves for me when we have finished. She might be able to see if Harry will ask me to marry him? She's pretty good at that. I can't do it though it's just tea leaves to me.

I need to sit up. I can feel the sunshine on my face as I gaze along the promenade. I can see him in the distance. I recognise his walk. As he gets closer his eyes sparkle and he smiles his beautiful smile. His hand is held out to me.

"Will you walk with me?"

My heart surges with joy. This is all I want. At last, my Harry. He's come back for me.

"Yes, I'll walk with you. I have been waiting and waiting for you to come."

About the Author

Joan Hallam was born and raised in Moss Side and Wythenshawe, Manchester. She is married with children and grandchildren.

As an interest, once she retired, she started to research her family history. Using her research, memories, handed down tales and, wanting to share with the rest of the family the story of her Grandma and Grandad she began to write this book.

It was with the help of the tutors and members of the Writing Well and Speaking Well groups in Wythenshawe Forum Library that she was encouraged to complete this timeless story.

Lightning Source UK Ltd.
Milton Keynes UK
UKHW020716220321
380773UK00013B/1120

9 781838 299309